あさのうた
Impressions of Morning

公益財団法人JAL財団=編
Edited by JAL Foundation

ブロンズ新社
Bronze Publishing

朝のうたをリレーしよう！

俳句集団『いつき組』組長　夏井いつき

三十年ほど前、私は中学校の国語教員をしていました。一年生の最初の教材は詩。詩人谷川俊太郎さんの「朝のリレー」です。きりんの夢を見るカムチャッカの若者、朝もやの中でバスを待つメキシコの娘、寝がえりをうつニューヨークの少女、柱頭を染める朝陽にウインクするローマの少年が次々に出てくる詩です。

谷川さんの詩の後半には、こんな詩句があります。

　ぼくらは朝をリレーするのだ
　経度から経度へと
　そうしていわば交替で地球を守る

世界の子どもたちが繋いでいく「朝のリレー」は、人と人、国と国、心と心を繋ぎます。地球の朝をリレーするとは、生きてここに在る喜びであり、当たり前の朝を迎えられる感謝であり、世界の人々と共有する地球への賛歌です。好きな作品が見つかれば、暗唱して下さい。声に出して味わって下さい。世界の子どもたちと一緒に、私たちの朝をリレーしていきましょう。

『地球歳時記　第十四巻』のテーマが「あさのうた」だと知ったとたん、私の脳裏には生徒たちと一緒に暗唱した詩「朝のリレー」が溢れるように蘇ってきました。

第十四巻となる本書にも、世界中の「あさ」が溢れています。光る朝、濡れる朝、嬉しい朝、悲しい朝、美しい朝、戦禍の朝、平和の朝、当たり前の朝など、様々な「あさ」の表情の中に、子どもたちの今が描かれています。

俳句＆ハイクは、世界で一番短い詩ですが、見事な伝達力を持っています。小さな場面を切り取ることで豊かな世界を表現し得る、それがこの詩形の力なのです。

本書の一ページ一ページをめくってみて下さい。ハイクという小さな詩を読み解く味方となってくれるのは、ほんの小さな光景や心情ですが、文字の向こうにある現実や希望へと想像の翼を広げてみましょう。想像力を杖として、ハイクの森を歩き出してみましょう、見まわしてみましょう。ハイクという小さな詩には、世界各国の子どもたちの今を生きる現場が生々しく息づいているのです。

＊「ハイク」：日本語の五七五で詠まれる「俳句」に対し、海外の母国語で詠まれる三行の詩を「ハイク」と表現しています。

はじめに

"Morning – Pass It On!"

Itsuki Natsui
President of the Itsuki-Gumi Haiku Society

About 30 years ago, I was teaching Japanese at a junior high school. On the first day of class for first-year students, we read a poem called Morning Relay by Mr. Shuntaro Tanikawa. In this poem we met a series of people from various parts of the world – a young man in Kamchatka dreaming of a giraffe, a young lady in Mexico waiting for a bus in the morning mist, a little girl in New York rolling over in her bed with a happy smile, and a boy in Rome winking at a ray of morning light touching the top of an ancient column.

The moment I was informed that the theme for Volume 14 of Haiku by World Children would be "Impressions of Morning", my mind was overflowing with memories of reciting this poem with my students.

The fourteenth volume of this haiku and picture anthology is also filled with mornings from around the world. The various mornings compiled in this book – shining mornings, rainy mornings, joyful mornings, sad mornings, beautiful mornings, war-ravaged mornings, peaceful mornings, and ordinary mornings – capture the faces of children living their everyday lives. Haiku - whether the traditional 17-syllable poem composed in Japanese or the three-line poems composed in other languages - is the world's shortest form of poetry and is a powerful way to communicate. The power of haiku lies in its ability to convey depth and richness by capturing small scenes of our daily life.

I encourage you to savor every page of this book. Your imagination is the key to appreciating haiku. The works contained in this book capture brief moments and sentiments in a person's everyday life, but when you expand the wings of your imagination, you will gain a glimpse into the realities and hopes that lie beyond the few words you see on paper. Step into the forest of haiku, with your imagination as your walking stick, and have a look around. You will find that this short form of poetry pulsates with the energy of children all over the world, living in everyday real-life situations.

In the latter part of Mr. Tanikawa's Morning Relay, there are such phrases as:

We are relaying morning
From longitude to longitude
As taking turns to protect the earth

This "relay" in which children pass the morning around the world links people to people, country to country and heart to heart. Passing the mornings around the earth is an expression of the joy of living in the moment and of gratitude for being able to greet each morning, and a hymn to the earth that we share with our fellow citizens of the world. When you find your favorite haiku, I encourage you to recite and savor it out loud. Let us pass on our mornings together with children around the world.

1章 あさのかがやき
Morning Glories

夜明(よあ)けが
夜(よる)の闇(やみ)を破(やぶ)って
新(あたら)しい日(ひ)がうまれる

The dawn of the day
Breaking the darkness of night
A new day is born

• • • • • • • • •

Shayna Neo
age10　Female　Singapore（シンガポール）

輝かしい夜明け
大きな光の海が
暗闇を征服する

The glorious dawn
A vast sea of radiance
Conquers the darkness

・・・・・・・・・

Athalia Fubara
age 14　Female
Ireland（アイルランド）

Pearl necklace on the eaves
Shining in the morning sun
Before tears

Pärlikee räästas
Särab hommikupäikeses
Enne pisaraid

· · · · · · · · · ·

Liiljan Veske
age12　Female
Estonia（エストニア）

軒先に真珠の首飾り
朝日に輝いている
涙になる前に

As soon as the sun rises
In the sky of Mongolia
The earth will be glad

Монголын тэнгэрт
Наран мандахад
Ертөнц хүртэл баясана

· · · · · · · · · ·

Э.Чилүүгэн
Chiluugen E
age13　Male
Mongol（モンゴル）

モンゴルの空に
太陽が出るとすぐ
大地は大喜び

This morning quivers
A new beginning breathes
Inside me, too

Jutro treperi
Novi početak diše
I u meni

· · · · · · · · · ·

Laura Bizjak
age14　Female
Croatia（クロアチア）

朝がふるえる
新しいはじまりが息をする
私の中でも

Grasshopper twitters in the dew
Thoughts in the head
As alarm-clocks

Žiogas rasoje
Galvoje čirškia mintys
Lyg žadintuvai

Ieva Malinauskaitė
Ieva Malinauskaite
age13　Female
Lithuania（リトアニア）

朝露に虫が鳴く
頭が働きだす
目ざましが鳴って

Smelling the morning dew
Morning
Is your other name

Dišiš po jutranji rosi!
Jutro je tvoje
Drugo ime

Tjaša Špec
age10　Female
Slovenia（スロベニア）

朝露のにおいがする
朝は
あなたのもうひとつの名前

On the Horizon
Sun rises as Moon sets to
Start a new morning

Catherine Mae B. Basto
age11　Female
USA（米国／グアム）

水平線に
月が沈んでお日さまが昇る
新しい朝がはじまる

よがあけた
あさだよみんな
めをさまして

The dawn ascending
We are all morning
Wake up now people

Լույսը բացվեց
Մենք բոլորս առավոտ ենք
Արթնացեք մարդիկ

・・・・・・・・・

Արաքս Վարժապետյան
Araks Varzhapetyan
age 6　Female
Armenia（アルメニア）

大(おお)きなブラジル松(まつ)が
朝日(あさひ)を魅了(みりょう)する
小(ちい)さな私(わたし)

Tall brazilian pine
Enchants the aurora
And I feel tiny

Grande araucária
Que encanta a aurora
Sinto-me pequenina

● ● ● ● ● ● ● ●

Milena Mayara Tyski de Oliveira
age13 Female
Brazil（ブラジル）

Start the day
Yesterday is over
Rise again

Simulan ngayon
Tapos na ang kahapon
Muling bumangon

· · · · · · · · · ·

Mary Jane Bayawa
age15　Female
Philippines（フィリピン）

一日をはじめよう
昨日は終わった
さあ起きろ

Flock of birds
Rooster song
The murmur of the water

Stol de păsări
Cântecul cocoșului
Murmurul apei

· · · · · · · · · ·

Giuglea Eliza
age 14　Female
Romania（ルーマニア）

鳥の群れ
雄鳥の声
水のざわめき

Dawn
Mommy embraces me
And I dream again

Mattino
Mamma mi abbraccia
Di nuovo a sognare

· · · · · · · · · ·

Aurora Buonaurio
age13　Female
Italy（イタリア）

夜明け
ママが私を抱きしめる
私はまた夢をみる

きれいで赤い
朝（あさ）は
でっかい

Beautiful and red
The morning
Is immense

Bello e rosso
Il mattino
È immenso

Yuta Furukawa
age 9　Male
Italy（イタリア）

お日（ひ）さま おはよう
朝（あさ）の光（ひかり）とあたたかさをくれて
ありがとう お日（ひ）さま

Hello, little sun
You spread morning light and heat
Thank you, little sun

Kate Natalie Kwan Kai-en
age 8　Female
Singapore（シンガポール）

すてきなあさ
おひさまにてをのばそう
もっとまえに

Lovely morning
Reaching out towards the sun
And forwards

Labs rīts
Tiecos pret sauli un augu
Uz priekšu

Rolands Taraņenko
Rolands Taranenko
age 6　Male
Latvia（ラトビア）

The sun comes out
When you hear cock-a-doodle-doo
A new day has come

Mặt trời mọc lên cao
Chú gà trống cất lên tiếng gáy
Một ngày mới bắt đầu

・・・・・・・・・

Đỗ Ngọc Anh
Do Ngoc Anh
age13　Female
Vietnam（ベトナム）

日が昇(のぼ)り
雄鳥(おんどり)が時(とき)を告(つ)げると
新(あたら)しい日(ひ)がくる

Hello to sunrise
In the blue cloud you shall fly
Come another day

・・・・・・・・・

Marianne Handoko
age 7　Female
Australia（オーストラリア）

日(ひ)の出(で)にごあいさつ
青(あお)い雲(くも)にうかぶのね
またきてね

The wind is blowing, leaves are agitated
Clear dew drops and fresh air
I wish there was only morning

ลมพัดใบไม้พลิ้ว
น้ำค้างใสอากาศสดชื่น
อยากให้มีแค่เช้า

บุษมาศ นุชไธสง
Bootsamas Nuchtaisong
age11 Female
Thailand (タイ)

風が吹いて葉っぱが揺すられ
透き通った露と新鮮な空気
ずっと朝ならいいのに

日の出
早朝に暗やみからひとすじの光
一日がはじまる

Sunrise starts the day
In the early morning serving as a beacon of light
For the dark

清晨的日出
黑暗中的一盞明燈
一天的開始

....

林 大鈞
Max Lin
age 9　Male
Taiwan（台湾／台北）

The earth will be heated
By the sunshine in the wide field
The morning is coming up

Огторгуйн уудам талд
Дэлхийн нарны элчинд тайтгарна
Ертөнцөд өглөө айсуй

....

Т.Номин
Nomin T
age13　Female
Mongol（モンゴル）

大草原の陽光が
地球をあたため
朝がはじまる

Listen to this sound
The hidden serenity of
The morning rush

Ecoute ce son
La sérénité cachée
Du matin pressé

....

Parrot Astrid
age11　Female
Senegal（セネガル）

きいてこの音
目にはみえない静けさの
朝が急いでやってくる

Light spreads, darkness fades
The city is half awake
Lights shine, flicker on

•••••••••

Millie-Mae Barber
age12　Female
UK（英国）

光が広がり闇が消える
街は半分目ざめ
灯りがまたたく

The earth by different colours
Humans by the colour of desire
Life by the colour of success

Орчлон олон өнгөөр
Хүмүүнийг хүслийн өнгөөр
Амьдралыг амжилтын өнгөөр

•••••••••

М.Билгүүндалай
Bilbuundalai M
age13　Female
Mongol（モンゴル）

地球はさまざまな色で
人間は願望の色で
人生は成功の色で

When it is morning
Next to the window sill
I play guess-the-color

Sabah olunca
Pencere kenarında
Renk tutarım ben

•••••••••

Güler Kaya
Guler Kaya
age10　Female
Turkey（トルコ）

朝になったら
わたしは窓辺で
色をつかまえるわ

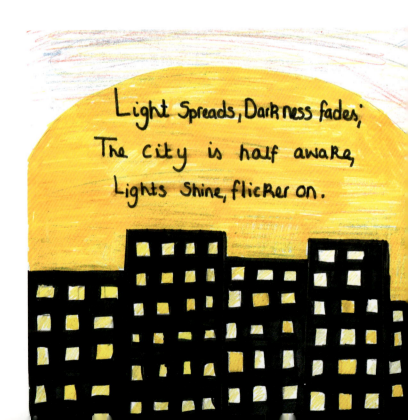

As my dreams leave me
I blindly open my eyes
And peer at the sun

●●●●●●●●

Jaqueline Boyce
age12　Female
USA（米国／サンディエゴ）

夢からさめて
ゆっくり目を開き
太陽をじっとみつめる

暗い夜
月が姿を変える
大きな夜明けに

Dark night
The moon is transforming itself
In an immense dawn

La notte oscura
La luna si trasforma
Nell'alba immensa

• • • • • • • • •

Ludovica Moriconi
age 8　Female
Italy（イタリア）

Playing peek-a-boo
Painting the sky shades of pink
My rays start your day

● ● ● ● ●

Cordelia Oh
age12　Female
Singapore（シンガポール）

いないいないばあ
空を ピンクに染めて
私の光があなたの一日をはじめる

The morning has come
Beautiful, inimitable
Joyful faces

Առավոտը բացվեց
Գեղեցիկ, անկրկնելի
Երջանիկ դեմքեր

● ● ● ● ●

Էլլա Մարգարյան
Ella Margaryan
age12　Female
Armenia（アルメニア）

朝がきた
ふたつとない美しさ
幸せな顔

The sadness in deep darkness
Will be disappeared
By the bird singing

Түнэр харанхуйн
Уйтгар гунигийг
Шувуудын жиргээ үргээнэ

● ● ● ● ●

Б.Нандин-Эрдэнэ
Nandin-Erdene B
age12　Female
Mongol（モンゴル）

深い闇の中の悲しみは
消え去るでしょう
鳥の歌声とともに

I hear morning
Light warms the face
Dew disappears

Dzirdu rītu
Gaisma silda seju
Nožūst rasa

● ● ● ● ●

Elīza Kupruka
Eliza Kupruka
age14　Female
Latvia（ラトビア）

朝がきこえる
光が顔をあたためる
朝露が消える

動物園の象
干し草の朝ごはんを食べながら
ホームシック

Elephant at zoo
Is eating hay for breakfast
Feeling homesick

Слон в зоопарке
Завтракает сеном
Грустит о доме

Анри Имнадзе
Anri Imnadze
age13　Male
Russia（ロシア）

ひとしきり黒い煙が昇り
汽笛の音で朝の静けさが破られ
美しい一日がはじまる

A blast of black smoke springing up
The train whistle distrubs the silence in the morning
Starting up a beautiful day

一陣黑煙竄起
鳴笛聲劃破了清晨的寧靜
啟動美好一天

蕭 伶珊
Hsiao Ling-Shan
age12　Female
Taiwan（台湾／高雄）

朝の空
カラスが飛んでいる
黒点みたい

In the sky of morning
The crow flies
Like a black spot

Өглөөний тэнгэрт
Хэрээ нисэх нь
Хар толбо мэт

М.Сүндэрмаа
Sundermaa M
age11　Female
Mongol（モンゴル）

雄鳥は鳴き
空が赤くなると鳥が歌いだす
暗黒のベールは消えた

Cocks crow, birds chirp as
The sky wears a crimson look
The dark black veil gone

Ruhee Parelkar
age13　Female
India（インド）

As I gaze away
The Heron it does well
Into the morning

Aditi Sing
age 13　Female
UK（英国）

私（わたし）が目（め）をそらすと
白鷺（しらさぎ）も同（おな）じようにそらし
朝（あさ）の中（なか）に目（め）を向（む）けた

フクロウは王座を
雄鳥に明けわたした
証人は太陽の私

The owl passed his throne
To Mister Rooster
The sun is my witness

Baykuş tahtını
Bay horoza devretmiş
Şahidim güneş

Ezgi Boz
age13　Female
Turkey（トルコ）

空が明るくなる
鳥は翼に朝をのせて
世界に羽ばたく

The sky brightens
A bird carries on its wings
Morning to the world

Šviesėja dangus
Ant sparnų paukštis neša
Pasauliui rytą . . .

Ugnė Legytė
Ugne Legyte
age12　Female
Lithuania（リトアニア）

鳥の歌声が
お日さまを呼んで
すべてを明るくする

The birds' song
Is calling the sun
Making everything bright

Tiếng chim gọi mặt trời
Bóng tối lụi tàn, hừng đông ửng đỏ
Soi sáng khắp muôn nơi

Lưu Quang Trung Hiếu
Luu Quang Trung Hieu
age14　Male
Vietnam（ベトナム）

鳥たちがさえずる
小鳥かコウノトリだろうか
ほかの鳥たちも目をさます

Birds are singing
Is it finch or stork
Others are waking up

Laulavad linnud
Kas siis leevike või kurg
Ärkavad teised

Robin Kaiküll
Robin Kaikyll
age12　Male
Estonia（エストニア）

The early morning sends away the darkness of yesterday
Bringing today the bright sunshine and infinite hope
Like a mother embracing her child

清晨送走了昨日的黑暗
為今日帶來了明亮的陽光和無限希望
如同媽媽般擁抱著心肝

張 宇萱
Chang Yu-Hsuan
age10　Female
Taiwan（台湾／台北）

朝は昨日の闇を押しやって
明るいお日さまとあふれる希望を連れてくる
子どもを抱くお母さんのように

Starting off the day
Don't want to get out of bed
Mom's hug wakes me up

Rylan Tanaka
age 8　Male
USA（米国／ハワイ）

一日がはじまるよ
ベッドから出たくないな
ママに抱かれて目がさめる

The scent of mom
Sleeping on her chest
Sun, don't rise!

Anne kokusu
Göğsünde uyuduğum
Sen doğma güneş

İlayda Ecelioğlu
Ilayda Ecelioglu
age 7　Female
Turkey（トルコ）

お母さんのにおい
その胸で眠った
昇らないで太陽

静かな朝露は
いつもよりしっとり
足がひんやり

The calm morning dew
Is more dewy than ever
Crisp cold under feet

● ● ● ● ● ● ● ● ●

Faith Tanaka
age 7　Female
USA（米国／ハワイ）

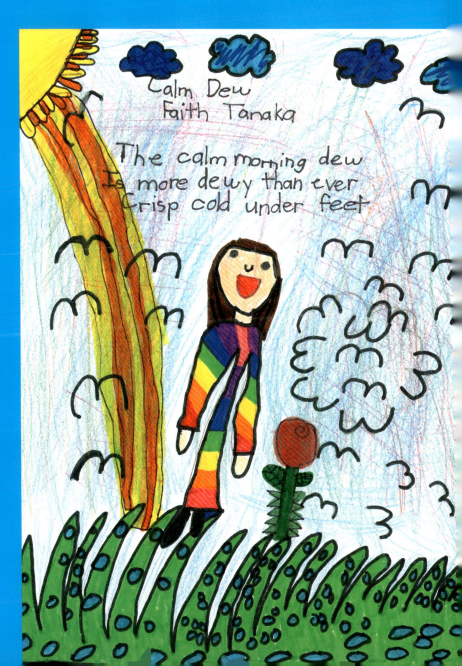

ゆっくりと日が昇り
静かな大地を照らす
道端の木々が頭を垂れる

The sun rising slowly
Shedding light on the quiet earth
Roadside trees bending their heads

太阳慢慢的升起
照耀在安静的大地上
道旁的树低垂着

罗 青青
Luo Qingqing
age13　Female
China（中国／大連）

一日がはじまった
永遠の愛とともに

Started a day
With eternal
Love

Mulanya Hari
Kasih Sayang Bersemi
Kekal Abadi

Maisara Bt Hashim
age10　Female
Malaysia（マレーシア）

大きく開いた目
お日さまが私を誘い
私は呼び声に応える

Eyes are wide open
The sun, it entices me
I answer its call

Cerila Rapadas
age13　Female
USA（米国／グアム）

Sun brightens my room
As it slips through my curtains
A new beginning

･････････

Jack Lambert
age 9 Male
USA（米国／サンディエゴ）

太陽がカーテンの隙間から
ぼくの部屋を明るくする
新しいはじまり

Sunshine bright
Illuminate my memory
Giving a good luck

Mentari Bangun
Menyinari Pagi Ku
Limpah Rezeki

･････････

Amni Nisrina Bt Akmal
age11 Female
Malaysia（マレーシア）

輝く太陽
記憶を照らして
幸運を招く

Rising once again
Giving us another chance
Do not be afraid

･････････

Kaitlyn Uemoto
age13 Female
USA（米国／ハワイ）

日が昇る
またチャンスがやってくる
恐れるな

When it is morning
Everything in its place
Me and my brother

Sabah olunca
Herşey yerli yerinde
Kardeşimle ben

İlknur Hilal Elitaş
Ilknur Hilal Elitas
age13　Female
Turkey（トルコ）

朝(あさ)になったら
なにもかもぜーんぶ、もとのまま
弟(おとうと)も私(わたし)も

A fresh new morning
Sunlight shines through my window
Time to learn new things

Mia Lau
age 8　Female
USA（米国／ハワイ）

気持(きも)ちいい新(あたら)しい朝(あさ)
窓(まど)からお日(ひ)さまの光(ひかり)
新(あたら)しいことを学(まな)ぶとき

Shoes are pacing
Reluctantly to school
Tearful morning

Pėdina batai
Nenoriai į mokyklą
Ašarų rytas

Rimvydas Mickus
age13　Male
Lithuania（リトアニア）

靴(くつ)をひきずって
しぶしぶ学校(がっこう)へ
涙(なみだ)の朝(あさ)

The smell of breakfast
Birds chirping by my window
"Rise and shine" Mom says

Renee Liang
age13　Female
USA（米国／ロサンゼルス）

朝ごはんのにおい
鳥たちが窓辺で鳴いて
「起きて輝くのよ」とママが言う

光が霧を消し
お日さまが農民を照らす
新しい日がきた

The light clears fog
Sunlight is shining on the farmers
A new day has come

Sáng xua tan sương mù
Mặt trời chiếu rọi người nông dân
Một ngày mới đã lên

Nguyễn Hà An
Nguyen Ha An
age13　Female　Vietnam（ベトナム）

Darkness has gone
Light shines through
Wow, a surprise

어둠이 가고
빛이 쏟아지듯 와
그게 신기해

· · · · · · · · ·

정 예담
Jeong Yedam
age10　Female
Korea（韓国）

闇が去り
光が降りそそぐ
わぁなんて不思議なの

新しい朝
去りゆく月よさようなら
鮮やかな露

A new rising morning
Farewell frightened moon
Fresh dew!

Nou matí naixent
Adéu lluna espantada
¡Fresca rosada!

· · · · · · · · ·

Alba Aparicio Nériz
age15　Female
Spain（スペイン）

Every morning is new
Every day is nice
Every staying is good

Өглөө болгон шинэхэн
Өдөр болгон гоёхон
өнжих бүрт сайхан

· · · · · · · · ·

Х.Гүнтөмөр
Guntumur Kh
age 9　Male
Mongol（モンゴル）

朝は新しい
毎日すてき
いつでも楽しい

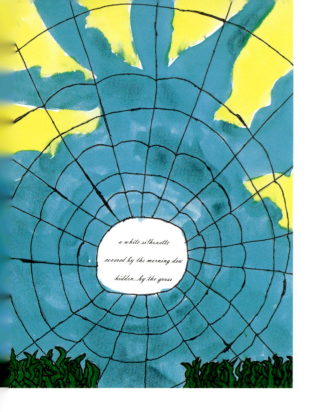

The Moon is desolated and grey
When I wake up, it is the most beautiful
And glows in the dark

Luna je pusta in siva
Ko se zbudim, je to najlepše
Kar sije v temi

・・・・・・・・・

Klara Lužnik
age 12　Female
Slovenia（スロベニア）

灰色のわびしい月
目ざめるとそれは
闇に輝く一番美しいもの

A white silhouette
Covered by the morning dew
Hidden, by the grass

・・・・・・・・・

Daniel Bouligny
age11　Male
USA（米国／シカゴ）

白いシルエット
朝露におおわれ
草に隠れて

Midnight wanders for
Dreams fade into morning mist
Rise and join the day

・・・・・・・・・

Alex Kalogerakis
age15　Male
UK（英国）

真夜中にさまよい
朝もやに消える夢
起きて一日をはじめよう

It is the game of nature
Which becomes dark in the night
And shows its beauty as the sun rise

Avni Sethi
age10　Female
India（インド）

自然のゲーム
夜には暗くなり
日の出とともに美しさをみせる

Small dewdrops at dawn
Playing hide-and-seek on petals
Sunshine is feared

清晨小露珠
花瓣上面捉迷藏
就怕见阳光

吴 安卓
Wu Anzhuo
age10　Female
China（中国／上海）

早朝の玉の露
花びらの上でかくれんぼ
太陽の光をおそれてるのね

Calm breath
Of a soft morning
Blooming lily

Calmo respiro
Di un soffice mattino
Giglio fiorente

Elena Francescatto
age13　Female
Italy（イタリア）

やわらかい朝の
静かな息
百合が咲く

Misty mountain morning
Breeze is blowing while birds are singing
Silhouette appears little by little

晨雾绕山林
微风轻拂鸟儿鸣
徐徐现人影

• • • • • • • • •

叶 振阳
Ye Zhenyang
age10　Male
China（中国／上海）

朝霧は山林めぐり
そよ風吹いて鳥は鳴く
徐々に人影が

A bird is singing
On the tree branch
A cloudless morning

O pasăre cântând
Pe creanga copacului
Dimineaţă fără nori

• • • • • • • • •

Pacea Ion
age 13　Male
Romania（ルーマニア）

木の枝で
鳥がさえずる
雲ひとつない朝

目がさめた
いっしょうけんめいお祈りをする
感謝をこめて

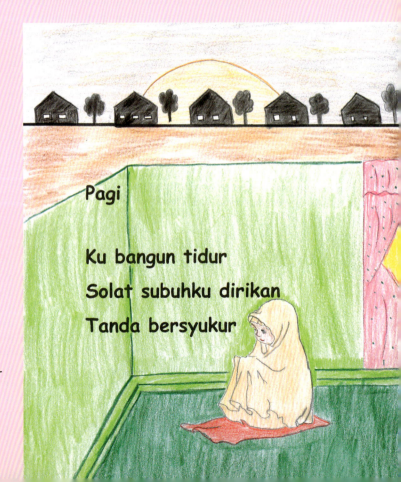

Woke up from sleep
Praying so hard
With gratitude

Pagi Ku Bangun Tidur
Solat Subuhku Dirikan
Tanda Bersyukur

• • • • • • • • •

Nur Humaira Bt Rhyrun Anuar
age 9　Female
Malaysia（マレーシア）

日の出
風が髪をなびかせ
雲が流れる

Sunrise
The wind blows through my hair
The clouds are drifting

Ein Sonnenaufgang
Der Wind fährt mir durchs Haar
Die Wolken ziehen vorbei

••••••••

Lilly Dörschel
age11　Female
Germany（ドイツ）

私の町の朝
雄鳥が鳴いて
新しい日がはじまる

Moring in my hometown
When you hear cock-a-doodle-doo
When a new day has come

Buổi sáng trên quê tôi
Khi chú gà cất lên tiếng gáy
Khi ngày mới bắt đầu

• • • • • • • • •

Vũ An Khanh
Vu An Khanh
age13　Female
Vietnam（ベトナム）

鳥が鳴き
ぼくらに朝がやってきて
眠気ふっとぶ

When the bird sings
The morning comes to us
Sleep steals away

Quand l'oiseau chante
Que le matin vient à nous
Le sommeil s'enfuit

• • • • • • • • •

Acogny Moussa
age11　Male
Senegal（セネガル）

朝起きて
疲れて窓をみる
日が昇る

In the morning I wake up
Looking out the window tiredly
Sunrise

Morgens wach ich auf
Schau müde aus dem Fenster
Die Sonne geht auf

• • • • • • • • •

Arwyn Schenk
age11　Male
Germany（ドイツ）

戦争や暴力があっても
日の出をごらん
諦めちゃ駄目だってこと忘れないで

Even though there is war and violence
Look at the sunrise
And do not forget to never give up

Zelfs als er veel oorlog en geweld is
Kijk naar de zonsopgang
En vergeet niet om nooit op te geven

• • • • • • • • • •

Nasya Weigand
age12　Female
Netherlands（オランダ）

Slow rising red light
Sheds beauty on night ashes
Sins are forgotten

• • • • • • • • • •

Chantelle Esper
age15　Female
Ireland（アイルランド）

ゆっくり昇る赤い光
夜の灰の上に美しさを放ち
罪は忘れられる

It is such a lonely morning
Our parents quarrelled late at night
We must be starving, my little sister

เช้านี้ช่างเงียบเหงา
พ่อแม่ทะเลาะกันกลางดึก
อดข้าวกันแล้วน้อง

• • • • • • • • • •

ชยุต บุญศรีวงศ์
Chayut Boonsriwong
age11　Male
Thailand（タイ）

なんてさびしい朝
両親がゆうべ遅くけんかした
飢え死にしそうだね 妹よ

Alarm clock is ringing
I knock it down from my bedside table
But it's still ringing

Budilka zvoni
Jo sklatim dol z omare
Pa še kar zvoni

・・・・・・・・・

Denis Jereb
age15　Male
Slovenia（スロベニア）

目ざまし時計が鳴っている
ベッドの横の机から叩きおとす
でもまだ鳴っている

Good morning Viet Nam . . . !
A beautiful country
Peaceful country

Chào buổi sáng Việt Nam...!
Đất nước Việt Nam vô cùng đẹp
Là đất nước hòa bình

・・・・・・・・・

Lã Vũ Bảo Châu
La Vu Bao Chau
age13　Female
Vietnam（ベトナム）

おはようベトナム！
美しい国
平和な国

Face of crimson fire
Rises above the mountains
River flows like song

・・・・・・・・・

Audrey Leona Harjanto
age14　Female
USA（米国／ロサンゼルス）

深紅の炎の顔が
山の上に昇る
川は歌うように流れる

おひさまは
ねぼうしないで
えらいよね

It never oversleeps…
The sun
Is wonderful!

● ● ● ● ● ● ● ● ●

三善 優花
Yuka Miyoshi
age 6　Female
Japan（日本）

フクロウの鳴き声が
窓の向こうで変わる
雄鳥の目ざましに

Owl's hoot
Changes behind the window
Into the rooster's alarm

Öökulli huige
Vahetub akna taga
Kuke alarmiks

● ● ● ● ● ● ● ● ●

Kadriina Krüüts
Kadriina Kruuts
age15　Female
Estonia（エストニア）

日が昇るとき
光とともに僕は起きて
自然の芸術をみるんだ

When the sun rises
I wake as light emerges
To see nature's art

● ● ● ● ● ● ● ● ●

Rocky Gao
age13　Male
USA（米国／ロサンゼルス）

39

Cold breeze, warm blanket
Smell of pancakes through the house
My world is awake

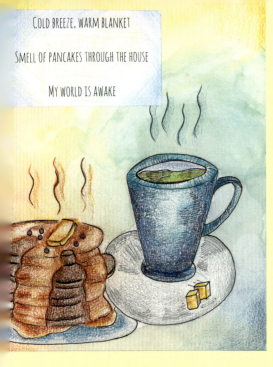

Cold breeze, warm blanket
Smell of pancakes through the house
My world is awake

● ● ● ● ● ● ●

Do Won Suh
age13　Female
USA（米国／ロサンゼルス）

冷たい風、あたたかな毛布
家じゅうパンケーキのにおい
私の世界が目をさます

No more shots (syringes) waking me up
Instead I feel my dad's warm hand
A morning I've long dreamt of

주사기 대신
따뜻한 아빠의 손
꿈 같은 아침

● ● ● ● ● ● ●

김시안
Kim Sian
age 8　Female
Korea（韓国）

注射で起こされるのはもういや
代わりにパパのあたたかい手が触れる
ずっと夢みているそんな朝

It will rain hard
The sun will shine afterwards
Oh! The rainbow!

Lloverá fuerte
El sol brillará depués
¡Ay, arcoíris!

● ● ● ● ● ● ●

Daniela Van Gestel
age 6　Female
Spain（スペイン）

どしゃぶりのあめがきて
おひさまがかがやく
わぁにじだ！

2章 きせつをかんじて
To Feel the Season

輝(かがや)いている朝(あさ)
花(はな)は咲(さ)きほこり
あざやかに美(うつく)しい

Bright morning
With flourishing flowers
Beautiful glow

Cerahnya Pagi
Bunga-Bunga Berkembang
Cantik Berseri

Muhammad Muizzuddin Bin Zaini
age 9　Male　Malaysia（マレーシア）

Cold morning
A good idea comes
Into my refreshed brain

Kylmä herätys
Aamu-uni ihana
Päätöksensä saa . . .

Jemina Raukamo
age15　Female
Finland（フィンランド）

寒い朝
頭が冴えて
アイデア浮かぶ

Cold morning awakes
Sun glistening on the snow
Tomorrow is spring

Külm hommik ärkab
Päike sillerdab lumel
Homme on kevad

Martti Meen
age14　Male
Estonia（エストニア）

寒い朝がはじまる
太陽が雪の上に輝く
明日はもう春だ

Winter morning—
An icicle is breaking
Near me

Dimineață de iarnă
Un țurțur spărgându-se
Lângă mine

• • • • • • • • •

Grigore Daria
age11　Female
Romania（ルーマニア）

冬の朝
一本のつららが折れる
わたしのそばで

These cold dark mornings
When I think it is the night
Winter tricks my mind

• • • • • • • • •

Emma O'Mahony
age12　Female
Ireland（アイルランド）

この冷たくて暗い朝
夜だと思ったのに
冬にはだまされる

Winter morning
Is playing the organ
In a small garden covered with snow

Žiemužės rytas . . .
Apsnigtam sodelyje
Groja vargonais

• • • • • • • • •

Simona Štombergaitė
Simona Stombergaite
age14　Female
Lithuania（リトアニア）

冬の朝が
オルガンを弾いている
雪のつもった小さな庭で

Sunny morning
A swallow fades away
In a warm haze

Saulainā rīta
Bezdelīga izgaist
Siltos dūmos

Elīza Valtere
Elyse Valther
age11　Female
Latvia（ラトビア）

晴れた朝
ツバメが消える
あたたかなもやの中へ

In morning flowers are blooming
Plants are growing
It's time to have fun out in the sun

Ann Joby
age12　Female
India（インド）

朝には花が咲き
植物は育っている
太陽の下で楽しむ時間よ

You, sun, rose up
Bees at work
The frog jumps away

Güneş doğdun sen
Arılar çalışırlar
Kurbağa zıplar

Nurdan Ahmetoğlu
Nurdan Ahmetoglu
age10　Female
Turkey（トルコ）

太陽さん、うまれたんだね
蜂たちは働きはじめ
蛙たちはとびはねるよ

Nice to look at
The sky change his colour
And sun rising

Indah　Dipandang
Langit Berubah Warna
Terbit Mentari

Nurul Najihah Bt Mohd Fariq
age12　Female
Malaysia（マレーシア）

空の色が変わるのや
日の出をみるのは
すばらしい

輝く露
朝日に出会いお喋り
一日を開く音符一つ二つ

A glistening dew
Meets with the morning sun
Opening the day with musical notes

말간 이슬
해를 만나 종알종알
하루를 여는 음표 한 개 두 개

최 서희
Choi Seohee
age10　Female
Korea（韓国）

Frosty morning dew
The humming of the birds too
Natures morning clues

凍るような朝露
鳥のさえずりも
自然からの朝のヒント

Tanya Singh
age12　Female
UK（英国）

Ripening raspberries
In white morning light
A tree cut down

Sirpsta avietės
Balto ryto šviesoje
Nukirstas medis

Ugnė Bačinskaitė
Ugne Bacinskaite
age12　Female
Lithuania（リトアニア）

熟したラズベリーの実
白い朝の光の中で
一本の木が切り倒される

Winter
Sun rises under the windowsill
Cat coming home

Ziema
Zem palodzes saullēkts
Mājās atgriežas kaķis

Dāvis Huškadamovs
Davis Huskadamovs
age13　Male
Latvia（ラトビア）

冬
窓より低く日が昇る
猫帰る

Chicken chucking
With sun rising
So peaceful

Kokokan Ayam
Fajar Nian Menyingsing
Damai Alamku

• • • • • • • • •

Nur Raif Bin Huzairi
age11　Male
Malaysia（マレーシア）

日の出とともに
にわとりが鳴いている
とても平和だ

Under fresh sunshine
Little insects are very happy
With their hardworking

清爽阳光中
勤劳的小虫虫们
幸福的生活

• • • • • • • • •

杨 程睿
Yang Chengrui
age 7　Male
China（中国／北京・河北省・安徽省）

さわやかな朝日の中で
働き者の小さな虫たちが
幸せにくらしている

I wonder . . .
In the morning sky
Still the moon

• • • • • • • • •

常盤 日和
Hiyori Tokiwa
age 7　Female
Japan（日本）

ふしぎだな
あさのおそらに
おつきさま

47

Silent nature
Shines in the morning dew
Mummy's kiss

Tiha narava
Sije v jutranji rosi
Poljub mamice

・・・・・・・・

Julija Vidmar
age 8　Female
Slovenia（スロベニア）

静かな自然が
朝露の中で輝く
ママのキス

Anointed by dandelion
Enchanted by the scarlet sun
The twilight zephyr

Խատուտիկով օծվեց
Արեգակով կախարդված
Ջերյունն արշալույսի

・・・・・・・・

Սևան Ղարիբյան
Sevan Gharibyan
age15　Male
Armenia（アルメニア）

たんぽぽで清められ
太陽に魅せられる
夜明けのそよ風

Sweet cherry blossom
Beautiful morning daydream
Fresh, new beginning

・・・・・・・・

Francesca Wilkinson
age15　Female
UK（英国）

あまい桜の花
美しい朝の空想
さわやかで新しいはじまり

Beautiful brazilian pines
With the azure jays
In the morning light

Lindas araucárias
Com as gralhas azuis
Na manhã de luz

・・・・・・・・

Adrian Gabriel Bento
age 9　Male
Brazil（ブラジル）

美しいブラジル松に
アオカケス
朝の光につつまれて

目の前に
広がる大きなりんごの木
なんて美しい朝

In front of me
A huge apple tree stands up
How beautiful the morning

Devant moi se dresse
Un enorme pommier
De si beau matin

● ● ● ● ● ● ● ● ●

Miclot Erwin
age 8 Male
France（フランス）

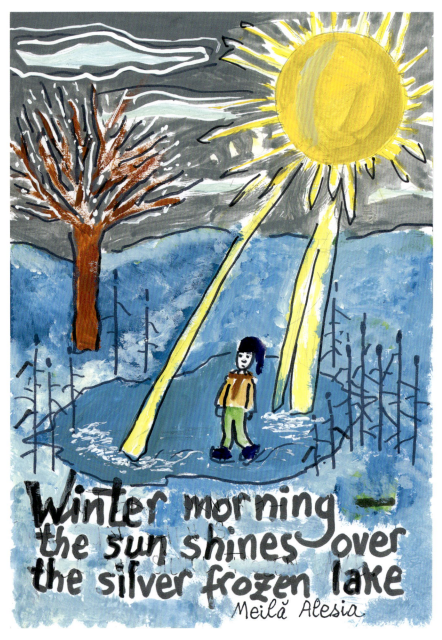

冬の朝
銀色に凍った湖を
照らすお日さま

Winter morning
The sun shines over
The silver frozen lake

Dimineață de iarnă
Soarele strălucește peste
Lacul de argint înghețat

•••••••••

Meilă Alesia
age11　Female
Romania（ルーマニア）

Brilliant freshness
Of an ice petal
Winter dawn

Fresco brillante
D'un petalo di ghiaccio
L'alba d'inverno

Giulia Petruccioli
age13　Female
Italy（イタリア）

氷の破片は
きらめくみずみずしさ
冬の夜明け

Warm, fuzzy blanket
Furry rug kisses my toes
Breathing in cold air

Olivia Kim
age 9　Female
USA（米国／ハワイ）

あたたかくてふわふわの毛布
毛皮のラグがわたしの足の指にキスする
冷たい空気を吸いこむ

Winter morning
Warm tea
My favourite book

Зимнее утро
Тёплый чай
Любимая книга

Dana Biktaševa
Dana Biktasheva
age13　Female
Latvia（ラトビア）

冬の朝
あたたかいお茶と
大好きな本

A cold morning
Took its white wings
Flew to the boundless

Սառը առավոտ
Սպիտակ թևերը առավ
Թռավ անհունը

Եվա Արարատյան
Eva Araratyan
age11　Female
Armenia（アルメニア）

寒い朝
その白い翼は
果てしなく

All night long
And in the early morning
The rain makes puddles

Cijelu noć
I rano ujutro
Kiša pravi lokve

Sara Podgajski
age12　Female
Croatia（クロアチア）

一晩中
そして早朝にも
雨が水たまりを作る

It is cold in the morning
Road sweeper sweats
I want to say "Thank you"

ยามเช้าอากาศหนาว
คนกวาดถนนอาบเหงื่อชุ่ม
อยากบอกขอบคุณนะ

รัฐพล ฤทธิ์ทรง
Ratthaporn Ritsong
age12　Male
Thailand（タイ）

寒い朝
道路掃除のおじさんは汗だく
「ありがとう」って言いたくなる

Skies of powdered gold
Glistens on the ocean floor
Making waves shimmer

Jasmine C. Pangelinan
age13　Female
USA（米国／グアム）

金粉を散らした空が
海一面に輝き
波をきらめかせる

The wind bell is ringing
Watching the dawn out of the window
Enjoying leisure and carefree

風鈴叮噹響
望著窗外的晨曦
悠閒又自在

毛 心祥
Mao Hsin-Hsiang
age12　Male
Taiwan（台湾／高雄）

風鈴が響いて
窓の外の夜明けをみながら
のんびり過ごす僕

As dew of morn
Falls upon the flowers
My soul rests within

Regina Gabriela Lage
age14　Female
USA（米国／ロサンゼルス）

朝の露が
花の上に結ばれて
心の中から和むの

The snowy owls sit
Snow flakes swirl near ever greens
A winter sunrise

Bronwyn Chernove
age 8　Female
Canada（カナダ）

白フクロウがとまっている
ときわ木に舞う雪片
冬の日の出

露のしずくに濡れて
足の指十本がもぞもぞ
私から花が咲いたみたい

In the dewdrops
Ten toes scurrying
I blossom

Kastetilkades
Sibavad kümme varvast
Puhkesin õide

Rea Haljasmäe
Rea Haljasmae
age12　Female　Estonia（エストニア）

You and me, together
We're crossing the sea of mind
Let's go to a new day

Jaz in ti. Skupaj
Greva čez morje misli
Greva. V nov dan

・・・・・・・

Eva Prevec
age13　Female
Slovenia（スロベニア）

あなたと私 一緒に
心の海をわたりましょう
さあいきましょう 新しい一日へ

The Dawn
Hide behind the moutain on the sea
Playing with the cloud

Bình minh trên mặt biển
Mặt trời lấp ló sau đỉnh núi
Đang vui đùa cùng mây

・・・・・・・

Phạm Thục Anh
Pham Thuc Anh
age13　Female
Vietnam（ベトナム）

夜明け
海の向こうの山に隠れて
雲と遊ぶお日さま

Sun rises with hope
Dress our brave heart with new look
Faith defeats sad mood

・・・・・・・

司徒 雲熙
Szeto Wan Hei Cato
age 9　Male
China（中国／香港）

希望に満ちて日は昇る
勇敢な心に新しい装いを
信念は悲しみを打ち負かす

空いっぱいに
幸せの香りが漂う
嬉しくなってわたしもにっこり

It fills the skies, with
Wafting scents of happiness,
With much joy, I smile

• • • • • • • • •

Emily Wong
age11　Female
USA（米国／ハワイ）

The morning sun
Like Mother of Earth is calling on dreaming earth
To greet the new day

早晨的太陽
像地球的母親喚醒正在夢中的大地
迎接ㄓㄢˇ新的一天

• • • • • • • • •

蔡 宇翔
Tsai Yu-Shiang
age10　Male
Taiwan（台湾／台北）

朝の太陽は
まるで地球のお母さん
新しい日を迎えるために　夢みる大地を起こす

Rainy morning
Rainbow takes its form
While the sun shines

Manhã com chuva
Arco-íris se formando
E o sol brilhando

• • • • • • • • •

Edenilson Daniel de Lima
age10　Male
Brazil（ブラジル）

雨の朝
虹がかかったよ
お日さまが出て

Dawn
It fills the skies, with
wafting scents of happiness,
with much joy, I smile.

お日さまが高く昇る
草原には朝露
新しい一日がやってきた

Sun rising up high
Morning dew on the grass floor
A new day has come

Joselle Garcia
age12 Female
USA（米国／グアム）

桜の木にメジロ
小人が輝くカーテンを少し開いて
鳥の声は遠くまで届く

White-eyes in the cherry tree
The elf slightly opens the shiny curtain
And the chirps of birds travel for miles

櫻花樹上的綠繡眼
小精靈拉開微光閃閃的布幕
鳴鳥聲傳數里遠

丘 少宇
Chiu Shao-Yu
age12 Male
Taiwan（台湾／台北）

命のひびき
動物の動き
でも私は動かない

The life's echo
Animal movements
But I'm still

Odmev življenja
Premikanje živali
A jaz mirujem

Eva Šubic
age13 Female
Slovenia（スロベニア）

東(ひがし)の王冠(おうかん)
金色(きんいろ)の綿毛(わたげ)
朝(あさ)のタンポポのそよ風(かぜ)

The crown of the east
Fleece of gold each morning's tease
Dandelions breeze

Poem Schway
age10　Female
USA（米国／サンフランシスコ）

Out in the garden
As the wind speaks to the grass
Melting . . . Spring comes home

Mabelle Choong
age11　Female
UK（英国）

庭(にわ)では
風(かぜ)が芝生(しばふ)に話(はな)しかけて
とけている…春(はる)がもどってきたよ

Following mommy to the flower market
I ask the calligrapher for a nice word
Beautiful peach flowers!

Theo mẹ đi chợ hoa
Ngày xuân xin chữ ông Đồ già
Mai đào khoe sắc thắm

Lê Hà Chi
Le Ha Chi
age13　Female
Vietnam（ベトナム）

ママと花市(はないち)へ
書家(しょか)にすてきな言葉(ことば)をお願(ねが)いする
きれいな桃(もも)の花(はな)！

58

Morning is nice
Spring came
Everything is happy

Өглөө бол сайхан
Хавар ирэв
Бүх зүйл аз жаргалтай

Г.Жаргалмаа
Jargalmaa G
age10　Female
Mongol（モンゴル）

朝はすてき
春がきた
みんな幸せ

A morning wakes
It screams aloud
The future spins

Jutro se zbudi
Na ves glas zakriči
Prihodnost se zavrti

Maja Žunič
age 7　Female
Slovenia（スロベニア）

朝がはじまる
大きな叫び声をあげる
未来が回りはじめる

The morning sun laughs
With carpet flying in the wind
How free and happy we are

清晨太阳笑
飞毯迎风飞得高
我们多逍遥

王 睿远
Wang Ruiyuan
age 7　Female
China（中国／北京・河北省・安徽省）

朝日は笑う
空飛ぶじゅうたんにのって
なんて自由で幸せなの

Light rain singing a song
Lots of flowers blooming and grass laughing as well
Animals running about

细雨在歌唱
百花盛开禾苗笑
动物竟自由

....

苏 彦臣
Su Yanchen
age 9　Male
China（中国／大連）

小雨が歌い
花がいっぱい草も笑う
動物たちは駆けまわる

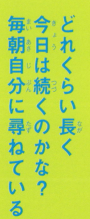

Best morning of all
Did Santa come to my house?
I run to the tree

....

Naomi Shim
age 7　Female
USA（米国／サンディエゴ）

一番いい朝
サンタさんはわたしの家にきたかな？
ツリーへまっしぐら

How long
Is today going to last?
I ask myself every morning

Koliko časa bo
Danes dan trajal?
Se vsako jutro sprašujem

....

Vida Krek
age10　Female
Slovenia（スロベニア）

どれくらい長く
今日は続くのかな？
毎朝自分に尋ねている

一月(いちがつ)の朝(あさ)
波(なみ)の泡(あわ)が
わたしの足(あし)に届(とど)く

January morning
The foam of the waves
Reaches my feet

Mañana de enero
La espuma de las olas
Llega a mis pies

Nikoleta Stefanova Micheva
age11 Female
Spain（スペイン）

青々(あおあお)とした川辺(かわべ)の草(くさ)
蜂(はち)とび蝶(ちょう)舞(ま)い蛙(かえる)とび
柳(やなぎ)は風(かぜ)にそよぐ

Tender grass along spring creek
All fairy-like creatures bustling with fun
Weeping willow swaying from breeze

青青河边草
蜂飞蝶舞蛙儿跳
柳叶乐弯腰

顾 辰瑜
Gu Chenyu
age10　Female
China（中国／上海）

Sun rising
Cheerful fowl
My heart rejoice

Terbitnya Pagi
Sang Unggas Keriangan
Hatiku Girang

・・・・・・・・・

Nur Arini Binti Mahazir
age 9　Female
Malaysia（マレーシア）

日が昇る
鳥たちが喜んでいる
わたしの心も喜んでいる

Good morning sunshine
Sakuras are in bloom
Peace is in the air

・・・・・・・・・

Katherine Reilly
age 9　Female
Canada（カナダ）

おはようお日さま
桜が咲いて
平和な感じ

Morning dew glitters
The garden's flowers bathe in the sunshine
Their fragrance coming with the wind

清晨雨露上
庭院花朵浴阳光
飘来阵阵香

・・・・・・・・・

刘 雨函
Liu Yuhan
age 11　Female
China（中国／北京・河北省・安徽省）

雨露残る朝
庭の花びらは日光を浴び
香りがだんだん漂ってくる

In a blue morning
With the raven's dark voice
Winter begins

U plavo jutro
Crnim glasom gavrana
Počinje zima

ゆううつな朝に
カラスの暗い声
冬がはじまる

Petar Mataušić
age 11　Male
Croatia（クロアチア）

Winter morning
I breathe out a puff
Like Godzilla

冬の朝
ゴジラのような
いきをはく

田頭 育人
Ikuto Tagashira
age 9　Male
Japan（日本）

Snow falling
Looks cold
But it's warm this morning

눈이 내려서
추울 것만 같아도
따뜻한 아침

雪が降り
寒そう
でもあたたかい朝

김 연수
Kim Yeonsu
age 9　Male
Korea（韓国）

雪の朝
シュガーバニーの脚が
コーヒーに溶けていく

Snowy morning
Sugar bunnies with steamy feet
Melting in coffee

Piesnidzis rīts
Kūpošām pēdām cukura zaķi
Kafijā kūst

● ● ● ● ● ● ● ● ●

Amanda Ancveire
age13　Female
Latvia（ラトビア）

お日（ひ）さまが出（で）ると
そこらじゅうに色（いろ）があふれる
一日（いちにち）の準備（じゅんび）ができた

When the sun is here
There is color everywhere
Ready for the day

· · · · · · · · ·

Ricardo Leon Guerrero II
age10　Male
USA（米国／グアム）

Colorful maple leaves falling on the country road
And I insert one in the book
To accompany me in a dream

穿著彩衣的楓葉
飄落在鄉間小路撿一片夾在書裡
陪我做夢…

· · · · · · · · ·

宋　昀禧
Sung Yun-Shi
age10　Female
Taiwan（台湾／台北）

田舎道（いなかみち）に散（ち）るもみじ
一枚（いちまい）を本（ほん）にはさむ
一緒（いっしょ）に夢（ゆめ）をみるために

Moon in the morning
Manoa Mountains so green
On the way to school

· · · · · · · · ·

Lulu Cole
age 7　Female
USA（米国／ハワイ）

朝（あさ）の月（つき）
学校（がっこう）にいくとき
マノア山（やま）はとっても緑（みどり）

Waking up early to greet the sun
Swim training all year round
Practicing hard to realize my dream

晨起迎光茳
泳訓伴我度四季
為夢想努力

王 如庭
Wang Ru-Ting
age13　Female
Taiwan（台湾／高雄）

早起きして光を迎え
四季を通して水泳訓練
自分の夢を叶える努力

A deep mist lingers
As the dawn clouds roll away
Across the North Sea

Eva Pellicci
age 8　Female
UK（英国）

深い霧
夜明けの雲が
北海をわたるとき

The Sun of dawn
Takes away the iceflowers
From my window

Koidupäikene
Viib kaasa jäälilled mu
aknaruutudelt

Andra Helena Toomet
age15　Female
Estonia（エストニア）

暁の太陽が
私の窓から
氷の花を持ちさる

朝の暗がりの中
月の影がゆらゆら揺れる
手で掬おう

At morning dusk
Reflection of the moon is trembling
I'll scoop it up with my hand

В сумерках утра
Дрожит отраженье луны
Рукой зачерпну

• • • • • • • • •

Михаил Матрук
Michael Matruk
age12　Male
Russia（ロシア）

今日は雨
わたしの鼻に朝の雨粒
幸せね

Rainy day today
Morning raindrops on my nose
Happy as can be

• • • • • • • • •

Violette Evangelynne Lovell Lie
age 8　Female
Singapore（シンガポール）

Morning mist
On the water of an old pond
A ray of sunshine

Brume du matin
Sur l'eau d'un vieil étang
Un rayon de soleil

• • • • • • • • •

Bentata Redouane
age 8　Male
France（フランス）

朝もや
古池の水面へ
陽の光

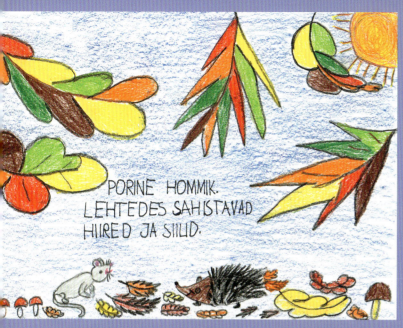

Muddy morning
Rustling in the leaves
Mice and hedgehogs

Porine hommik
Lehtedes sahistavad
Hiired ja siilid

Anette Leigri
age 7　Female
Estonia（エストニア）

泥だらけの朝
落葉の中でがさごそ
ネズミとハリネズミ

A tadpole looks for its mother
The sun smiles gently
Frogs are croaking

蝌蚪找妈妈
太阳公公微微笑
青蛙呱呱叫

郭 佳琳
Guo Jialin
age11　Female
China（中国／北京・河北省・安徽省）

オタマジャクシは母親さがし
お日さまはほほえみ
蛙はグァッグァッ鳴いている

Rooster crowing
Over the hills & mountains
An exquisite sound

Christopher Oki
age11　Male
USA（米国／ハワイ）

雄鳥が鳴く
丘や山の向こうで
すばらしい声だ

Facing the blue sky
I stretch my arms to hug
Seeing the new sun rising

蔚蓝的天空
展开双臂来拥抱
太阳初生了

••••••••

刘 嘉琪
Liu Jiaqi
age11　Female
China（中国／北京・河北省・安徽省）

青く晴れた空へ
両手を広げて抱きしめる
新しい太陽がうまれたよ

Sunny morning
Raindrop in the flower
Dries and disappears

Manhã de sol
Gota de água na flor
Vai desaparecendo

••••••••

Nauã Gabriel Wilke de Oliveira Lima
age 6　Male
Brazil（ブラジル）

はれたあさ
はなにあまつぶ
かわいてきえる

Summer day
Morning is hiding in my dreams
We are going to the beach

Poletni dan
Jutro se skriva v mojih sanjah
Vsi gremo na plažo

••••••••

Vid Jušič
age 8　Male
Slovenia（スロベニア）

夏の日
朝は夢に隠れている
ぼくたちは海岸にいくところ

70

In the fall morning
Under the branches of cherry tree
A golden leaf

Matin d'automne
Sous les branches du cerisier
Une feuille d'or

秋の朝
桜の枝の下に
金色の葉

Servon Raphaël
age 8　Male
France（フランス）

Drip drop drip drop, a sad song
As I walk closer I see
A little baby leaf weeping with sorrow

뚝 뚝 뚝 뚝 무슨 소리일까?
한 걸음 한 걸음 가보니
아기잎이 슬퍼 울고있네

ポロポロ、なんだろう？
そっと近づくと
小さな葉が悲しく泣いている

박 채윤
Park Chaeyun
age 7　Female
Korea（韓国）

Temple morning bells ring
Peach blossoms smile at dawn
Early fishermen busily hauling the net

山寺晨钟响
粉面桃花映朝阳
渔夫收网忙

山寺の朝の鐘の音
桃の花は朝日に映えて
漁師は網あげに忙しい

葛 方茗
Ge Fangming
age10　Female
China（中国／上海）

Sunlight is gradually seen
The sun shines over the ground
All things are living

天邊露曙光
太陽照遍大地上
萬物復生機

王 卓瑤
Wong Cheuk Yiu
age11　Female
China（中国／香港）

陽の光がだんだんとみえてくる
太陽が地面を照らし
すべての物は生きている

Rooster crows of joy
Dew has come down
Moist and brittle

Kukk rõõmust kireb
Maha tulnud kasteke
Niiske haprake

Liisa Tooming
age10　Female
Estonia（エストニア）

雄鳥が喜びの声をあげる
湿っぽくてはかない
露がおりている

Chirp, chirp, chirp
Waking everybody up
Is a tough job, too

金子 颯汰
Sota Kaneko
age11　Male
Japan（日本）

チチチチ
皆起こすのも
大仕事

Bright sun in the fall
The leaves falling from the trees
The colourful trees

秋の明るい太陽
散る木の葉
色とりどりの木々

Issis Hunt
age11　Female
Canada（カナダ）

公園で散歩
葉に光る朝露
今にも消えそう

Walking in the park
Shimmering dewdrops on leaves
Disappear too soon

・・・・・・・

Sarah Leaw Xuan Lin
age13　Female
Singapore（シンガポール）

To admire flowers in bloom
We come here when dawn comes
Butterflies dance gracefully

芳菲正满开
破晓只为看花来
彩蝶盈盈舞

満開の花をみに
夜明けにここにくる
軽やかに舞う蝶々

张 敏
Zhang Min
age11　Female
China（中国／北京・河北省・安徽省）

Sunbeam
Sandstorm ornaments
Are nearby to heart

Нарны цацраг
Угалзан хээ
Сэтгэлд дотно

太陽の光
心になじむ
砂嵐の装飾模様

・・・・・・・

О.Өнөболд
Unubold O
age14　Male
Mongol（モンゴル）

The rising sun
In the aromatic field
The joy of the countryside

Ургах наран
Анхилуун талд
Хөдөө нутгийн баясгалан

Б.Жавхлант
Javkhlant B
age13　Male
Mongol（モンゴル）

香りのよい草原に
昇る朝日
田園の喜び

Serene morning
The bird chirping
On a verdant mountain

Pagi Yang Hening
Burung Berkicau Riang
Gunung Menghijau

Muhammad Nabil Naim Bin Miski
age12　Male
Malaysia（マレーシア）

うららかな朝
鳥が鳴いている
新緑の山

Morning in spring
Wind breezes to my body
I am full of spirit

春天的早晨
微風輕吹我的身
讓我倍精神

劉 梓傲
Lau Tsz Ngo
age 9　Male
China（中国／香港）

春の朝
そよ風に吹かれて
元気いっぱい

The morning dew passing through
The spring thunder and flowing through the rhododendrons
Cleanses the dirtiness of earth

清晨的露水
穿過春雷流過了杜鵑
清除大地的汙穢

朝の露 春の雷は去り
シャクナゲから雫が落ちて
大地を清める

安 昕
An Sin
age11　Female
Taiwan（台湾／台北）

Morning dew
Is like pearls quietly shining
Under the sea

清晨的露珠
宛如海裡的珍珠
靜靜地閃耀

朝の露
海の底で静かに光る
真珠みたい

何 若綺
Ho Jo-Chi
age11　Female
Taiwan（台湾／台北）

Rosy clouds parted
Revealing beautiful light
Cranes swept past the skies

薔薇色の雲がわかれて
美しい光があらわれる
鶴が空を飛んでいく

Eunice Lim Yu Hann
age10　Female
Singapore（シンガポール）

White bread for pigeons
White gloves are strewing
Summer morning

Duoną balandžiams
Baltos pirštinės beria
Vasaros rytas

白いパンを鳩に
白い手袋が撒いている
夏の朝

Rosita Kalendaitė
Rosita Kalendaite
age13　Female
Lithuania（リトアニア）

朝露ひとつぶ
真珠散らばる葉の上で
てんとう虫ウロウロ

A dewdrop
On a beaded leaf
A ladybug moves

Une goutte de rosée
Sur une feuille perlée
Se déplace une coccinelle

Diagne Cheikh Tidiane
age14　Male
Senegal（セネガル）

Sunlight is gradually seen when waking up
Sun is shining when leaving home
I am ready to leave home now

醒時方破曉
出門已有日光照
儒子出門了

· · · · · · · ·

謝 瀚霆
Tse, Brendan Hon Ting
age 6　Male
China（中国／香港）

おきるとおひさまみえてきて
おうちをでたらぴかぴか
したくはできてるよ

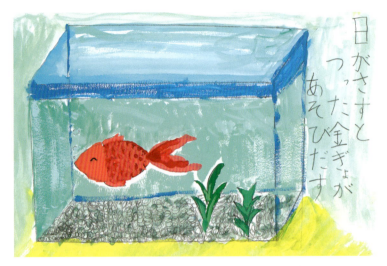

In morning sunlight
The goldfish I caught
Starts to play

· · · · · · · ·

金武 はな
Hana Kanetake
age 8　Female
Japan（日本）

日(ひ)がさすと
つった金(きん)ぎょが
あそびだす

The sun is rising
The grass is complete with dew
Daylight has come now

· · · · · · ·

Aahana Jagtiani Chadha
age 8　Female
UK（英国）

お日さまが昇(のぼ)る
草(くさ)に露(つゆ)がおりている
朝(あさ)の光(ひかり)がいま輝(かがや)きだす

3章 たのしいあさ
Funny Morning

蜂(はち)が起(お)きて
猫(ねこ)が起(お)きてにゃーと鳴(な)いて
お日(ひ)さま おはようございます

Bees getting up
And cats meowing after getting up
Good morning, Grandpa Sun!

蜜蜂起床了
貓咪起床喵喵叫
太陽公公好

劉 倚妃　Liu I-Pei
age 7　Female　Taiwan（台湾／台北）

A white cloud
Resembles a white foal
In the blue skies

Balts mākonis
Izskatās kā balts zirdziņš
Zilās debesīs

Vera Marija Sujetkina
Vera Maria Suetkina
age12　Female
Latvia（ラトビア）

白い雲
白い子馬に似て
青空の中

※ Braille work／点字・点図作品

In the rainy morning
Gold does not fall from the sky
But rather joy

Da manhã chuvosa
Ouro não cai do céu mas
Alegria sim

Fábio Miguel Brandão Lopes
age13　Male
Portugal（ポルトガル）

雨の朝
空から金は降ってこないけど
喜びは降ってくる

The moon hides you
All the blue night you sleep
Come back in the morning

La lune te cache
Toute la nuit bleue tu dors
Reviens le matin

Preira Océane
age11　Female
Senegal（セネガル）

月に隠され
紺色の夜に眠るあなた
朝になったら戻ってきてね

Look, it's finished
Sleep, you lover of dreams
The stars on their way

Sona erdi bak
Rüyanın aşkı uyku
Yıldızlar yolcu

Duygu Gürler
Duygu Gurler
age12 Female
Turkey（トルコ）

終わったんだね、ほら
夢の恋人、眠り
星たちも旅立つ

The Earth goes round and round
Your place is earlier than mine
Wake me up!

Trái đất luôn quay tròn
Bình minh nơi bạn sớm hơn tôi
Gọi tôi dậy, bạn ơi!

Ninh Quỳnh Như
Ninh Quynh Nhu
age13 Female
Vietnam（ベトナム）

地球はぐるぐる回る
あなたの所はもう朝ね
私を起こして

太陽が笛を吹くと
自然は歌い
空と大地は踊る

The sun played the flute
Nature sang a song
The sky and ground danced

Güneş flüt çaldı
Doğa şarkı söyledi
Gökle yer dansta

Zeynep Nisa Türkdönmez
Zeynep Nisa Turkdonmez
age 9 Female Turkey（トルコ）

Rooster is singing
Little chicks have already woken up
Morning begins

Gailis dzied
Cālēni jau pamodušies
Ir sācies rīts

Dārta Petkune
Darta Petkune
age14　Female
Latvia（ラトビア）

雄鳥が鳴いている
ひよこはもう起きだして
朝がはじまる

Early in the morning
I hear the noise of the cars
But I never hear noise of birds

De manhã cedinho
Ouço barulho de carros
De pássaros, nunca!

Carolina Correia Della Santina
age12　Female
Brazil（ブラジル）

早朝の車の騒音はきくけれど
鳥の騒音はきいたことがない

I went to the market in the morning
Back with a full basket of fresh fish, meat and vegetables
"Good boy!" my parents smiled

早晨去菜场
鱼肉蔬菜购满筐
爸妈夸我棒！

计 哲
Ji Zhe
age11　Male
China（中国／上海）

朝市にいき
魚肉野菜を籠いっぱい買い求め
両親にほめられた！

Hello Mr. Sun
Time to rise and shine your light
Up and up you go

Candice Candaso
age12　Female
USA（米国／グアム）

こんにちはお日さま
昇って輝く時間よ
さあ　昇って昇って

Morning of a championship
Family and friends in the field
Lots of supporters

Manhã de Campeonato
Família, amigos no campo
Muita torcida

・・・・・・・・・

Fernando Fernandes de Almeida
age14　Male
Brazil（ブラジル）

決勝戦の朝
フィールドには家族と友だち
たくさんのサポーター

Crisp snow lies tranquil
As the fiery sphere rises
Starving fox stalks hare

・・・・・・・・・

Reuben Flatman
age12　Male
UK（英国）

さらさらの雪が静かにひろがっている
火の玉が昇ると
飢えた狐が野ウサギにそっと近づく

The sun is rising
In the poppy field in the morning
An owl is coming back

Jau kyla saulė
Rytą aguonų lauke
Pelėda grįžta

・・・・・・・・・

Odeta Venslovaitė
Odeta Venslovaite
age15　Female
Lithuania（リトアニア）

日が昇り
朝の芥子畑に
フクロウが帰ってくる

朝の音
世界の夢
幸せな人々

Morning sound
The world's dream
Happy people

Som da manhã
O sonho do mundo
Pessoas felizes

Hugo Trindade
age15　Male
Portugal（ポルトガル）

草の上に落ちた
青（あお）りんご
朝（あさ）をおどろかす

Falling on the grass
An early apple
Startles the morning

Žolėn nukrito
alyvinis obuolys
Krūpteli rytas

Emilija Dorelytė
Emilija Dorelyte
age11　Female
Lithuania（リトアニア）

Deeper and deeper
I burrow into
The blanket cave

조금 조금만 몸이
기어 들어간다
이불동굴 속으로

이 채민
Lee Chaemin
age 9　Female
Korea（韓国）

少しずつ
体が潜りこんでいく
お布団の洞窟の中へ

The sound of the morning
Is the song of the lark
Spreading happiness about

清晨的叫声
是百灵鸟的歌唱
让幸福绵延

鲁 轩如
Lu Xuanru
age10　Female
China（中国／北京・河北省・安徽省）

朝の音は
ヒバリの歌
幸せがひろがる

Cloudy hare
Is running away from a crocodile
I'm walking to school

Облачный заяц
Бежит от крокодила
Я иду в школу

Николай Фролов
Nikolai Frolov
age11　Male
Russia（ロシア）

雲のウサギが
雲のワニから逃げている
ぼくは学校へ歩いてく

Good morning
Let's go to school
My friend

Selamat Pagi
Marilah Kawan-Kawan
Jom Ke Sekolah

Nur Lisa Suraya Binti Mohd Padhli
age12　Female
Malaysia（マレーシア）

おはよう
学校へいこう
私の友だち

Pages and pages
Of memories in your book
What page will come next?

・・・・・・・・・

Braden Nihei
age13　Male
USA（米国／ハワイ）

何ページも何ページも
あなたの本の中に詰まっている思い出
つぎはどんなページだろう？

All morning
A group of tree swallow
Come and go in the sky

Por toda a manhã
O bando de andorinhas
Vão e vêm no céu

・・・・・・・・・

Wagner Henrique Correia
age 9　Male
Brazil（ブラジル）

朝はミドリツバメの群れが
空をいったりきたり

A morning has come
Wake up!
Time for school!

Reng! Buổi sáng đến rồi
Mở mắt, thức dậy, một ngày mới
Nào, ta đi học thôi!

・・・・・・・・・

Trần Phương Thảo
Tran Phuong Thao
age14　Female
Vietnam（ベトナム）

朝がきた
起きて！
学校にいく時間！

A beautiful morning
Walking to school
For good knowledge

Pagi Yang Indah
Melangkah Ke Sekolah
Ilmu Terserlah

・・・・・・・・・

Aufa Rajihah Bt Mahadi
age10　Female
Malaysia（マレーシア）

美しい朝
学校へ歩いていく
勉強するために

朝になっても
ずっと一緒に夢みていたい
いつもあなたと

Morning, together
We will keep dreaming
Always with you

Mañana juntas
Seguiremos soñando
Siempre contigo

Paola Font Recio
age 9　Female
Spain（スペイン）

おはようお日さま
今日はすごいことが起こる
だからどこにもいかないで

Good morning sunshine
Today will be exciting
Please do not leave us

蔡 居宏
Choi Kui Wang
age 9　Male
China（中国／香港）

目がさめた
今日もしん長
のびたかな

I'm awake!
Am I taller
Than yesterday?

中川 桜子
Sakurako Nakagawa
age 6　Female
Japan（日本）

Wake up in sweet light
The morning glory is here
Lovely sight there is

Jessica Jin
age13　Female
USA（米国／グアム）

心地よい光に目がさめる
朝顔が咲いている
きれいな眺め

ベーコンのにおい
卵(たまご)のジュージューいう音(おと)
週末(しゅうまつ)は楽(たの)しい

The smell of the bacon
The sound of the eggs sizzling
The weekend brings joy

● ● ● ● ● ● ● ● ●

Melisa Aziminashemi
age13　Female
USA（米国／ロサンゼルス）

日(ひ)の出(で)は
水彩絵具(すいさいえのぐ)で
パステル色(いろ)の太陽(たいよう)の形(かたち)を整(とと)える

You are the sunrise
You paint with watercolours
Sculpting pastel suns

● ● ● ● ● ● ● ● ●

Niamh O'Farrell-Tyler
age15　Female
Ireland（アイルランド）

貝(かい)が開(ひら)く
白(しろ)いカモメが石(いし)の上(うえ)で
日(ひ)の出(で)をみている

Shell opens
White seagull sits on a stone
Watching the sun ascend

Gliemežvāks atveras
Balta kaija uz akmens
Rītā saullēktu vēro

● ● ● ● ● ● ● ● ●

Elza Līgute
Elsa Ligute
age13　Female
Latvia（ラトビア）

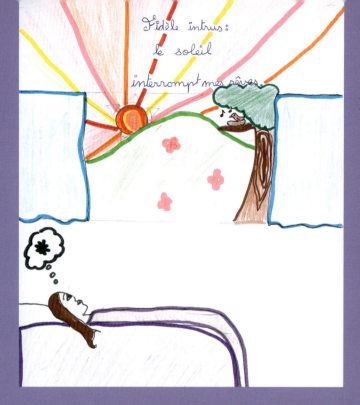

Reliable intruder
The sun
Disturbs my dreams

Fidèle intrus
Le soleil
Interrompt mes rêves

Ley London
age11 Female
Senegal（セネガル）

律義なちん入者
お日さま
わたしの夢のじゃまをする

I want to feel you
Warm from the sunlight
And fresh from your sleep

Harry Gupta
age13 Male
UK（英国）

僕は感じたい
お日さまのあたたかさ
目がさめたときのさわやかさ

First light—
On the potter's wheel
No finger prints

Prima lumină
Pe roata olarului
Nicio amprentă

Cazaciuc Fabiana
age 14 Female
Romania（ルーマニア）

最初の光
陶工のろくろに
指跡はない

お兄ちゃんが眠っている
私はおとなしくベッドの上に座り
狼のお面をかぶっている

My elder brother is sleeping
I'm quietly sitting on the bed
Wearing a wolf mask

Спит старший брат
Тихо сижу на кровати
В маске волка

Галина Тараканова
Galina Tarakanova
age13　Female　Russia（ロシア）

すみわたった朝の空気 宇宙にごあいさつ
羽ばたく鳥のさえずるメロディ
花と葉とともに朝を迎える

Clear and dew-cool air, say hello to the universe
A melody of chirping bird flapping his wing
Along with the dance of flowers and leaves I welcome morning

Bening embun, sejuk udara menyapa alam
Alunan nada ceririt burung kepakkan sayap
Seiring tarian bunga & daun Akupun menyambut pagi

・・・・・・・・・・

Mareta Rani Hapsari
age13　Female
Indonesia（インドネシア）

朝がきた
鳥たちは歌いはじめて
お日さまの光が大気を満たす

Morning has arrived
The birds are staring to sing
Sunshine fill the air

・・・・・・・・・・

Nazanin Rouhighodsinia
age14　Female
USA（米国／ロサンゼルス）

94

In a clear morning
I fly to the sky
Wings of imagination

Na manhã clara
Voei ao céu
Asas da imaginação

きれいな朝
私は空へ飛んでいく
想像の翼で

• • • • • • •

Alexsandra Nunes de Almeida
age13　Female
Brazil（ブラジル）

Sunlight is gradually seen
Should make use of today
To meet new challenges

曙光漸漸見
好好把握這一天
迎接新挑戰

太陽の光がだんだんみえてくる
今日を上手に使いましょう
新しい挑戦をしましょう

• • • • • • •

羅　浚詠
Law Chun Wing
age10　Female
China（中国／香港）

Early in the morning
Wings of a thousand colors
Are spreading love

Bem de manhãzinha
Estão as asas de mil cores
Espalhando o amor

朝早く
色とりどりの翼が
愛をひろげる

• • • • • • •

Margarida Campos
age12　Female
Portugal（ポルトガル）

Be a fisherman
May the morning wish you luck
Let's go to the horizon

Bir balıkçı ol
Rastgele desin sabah
Gidelim ufka

Nedimhan Özkol
Nedimhan Ozkol
age 6　Male
Turkey（トルコ）

りょうしになろう
たいりょうをいのってよ、あささん
さあいこう　すいへいせんをめざして

Shiny locks in the morning sun
Plait them in a braid
With a bright ribbon

Rīta saulē mirdzoši mati
Sapinu tos bizē
Iesienu lentu

Jasmīna Saule
Jasmin Saule
age 13　Female
Latvia（ラトビア）

朝日に輝く髪
三つ編みにして
明るい色のリボン

Going to school in a car
The traffic is so jammed
I wish my car could fly

นั่งรถไปโรงเรียน
บนถนนรถติดยาวเหยียด
อยากให้รถบินได้

สุดารัตน์ ปลาโพธิ์
Sudarut Parpo
age 12　Female
Thailand（タイ）

車で学校にいく
道路がすごく混んでいる
車が空を飛べたらいいのに

すてきな日
妖精(ようせい)たちが踊(おど)っているよ
花(はな)のいい香(かお)り

A beautiful day
Here elves and fairies flutter
With scenting flowers

美好的一天
精灵仙子在飞舞
花儿吐芬芳

徐 晗茜
Xu Hanxi
age 7　Female
China（中国／北京・河北省・安徽省）

Go to Chinese Restaurant in the morning
Shrimp dumpling, steamed rice roll, BBQ pork bun
All are in my tummy

早晨上茶樓
蝦餃、腸粉、叉燒包
全都在我肚

蕭 卓希
Siu Cheuk Hei Matt
age10　Male
China（中国／香港）

朝から中華料理店にいく
エビ餃子　腸粉　叉燒饅頭
みんなぼくのお腹の中

Shall we all be friends
On this beautiful morning
And play in the sun

Choh Shao Ken
age 8　Male
Singapore（シンガポール）

みんな友だちになろう
この美しい朝に
太陽の下で遊ぼう

The dark prince
To that dizzy bat
Morning is night

Karanlık prensi
Şaşkın yarasa için
Gecedir sabah

Maide Avcu
age15　Female
Turkey（トルコ）

暗闇の王子様
びっくりコウモリの
夜だね、朝は

Night is over
The first ray of sun
On the raven's wing

Naktis praėjo
Spindulys pirmutinis
Ant varno sparno

Urtė Strikaitė
Urte Strikaite
age14　Female
Lithuania（リトアニア）

夜が明けて
お日さまの最初の光が
カラスの翼に

朝(あさ)早(はや)く
畑(はたけ)の南瓜(かぼちゃ)が
お日(ひ)さまのふりをする

In the early morning
A pumpkin in the field pretends
To be the sun

Na polju bundeva
U rano jutro
Glumi sunce

Doris Krklec
age12　Female
Croatia（クロアチア）

すばらしい朝
鳥は幸せになり
そして雄鳥が鳴く

Incredible morning
The birds get happy
And the roosters sing

Incrível manhã
Os pássaros se alegram
E galos cantam

・・・・・・・・・

Daniele Pawlak
age13　Female
Brazil（ブラジル）

朝のハイキング
葉っぱの上に露がのっている
いい一日だなあ

Morning hike
Dew seen on leaves
It is a beautiful day

今早去行山
看見葉上的露水
美麗的人間

・・・・・・・・・

林 煒堯
Lam Wai Yiu
age10　Male
China（中国／香港）

朝がきた
ネズミを捕るのはわたしの楽しみ
さあ寝る時間

Morning has arrived
Catching mice is my hobby
Now it's time to sleep

・・・・・・・・・

Tan Xuan En
age10　Female
Singapore（シンガポール）

ギラギラの朝日
僕の雄鳥 時間だぜ
時を告げ 世界を起こせ

Glaring morning sun
My rooster, you know it's time
Crow out, wake the world

・・・・・・・・・

Phee Hong En Chrio
age12　Male
Singapore（シンガポール）

Seeing the morning sky
I flew all over the sky
And woke up to realize that I had fallen down from my bed

ได้เห็นฟ้ายามเช้า
ฉันบินไปทั่วท้องนภา
ตื่นมาฉันตกเตียง

・・・・・・・・

ธนพร รัตนพันธุ์
Thanaporn Rattanapan
age12　Female
Thailand（タイ）

朝の空をみながら
空じゅうを飛んでいたわ
目がさめたらベッドから落ちていた

The sun rises
And finds a lost toy
At the edge of the garden

Pateka saulė . . .
Sodo pakrašty mato
Pamestą žaislą . . .

・・・・・・・・

Eva Fišerytė
Eva Fiseryte
age14　Female
Lithuania（リトアニア）

お日さまが昇り
失くしたおもちゃがみつかる
庭の片隅

I got up in the morning
Butterflies colorful
Cat walks around

Tõusin hommikul
Liblikad värvilised
Kass kõnnib ringi

・・・・・・・・

Emma Jäär
Emma Jaer
age 5　Female
Estonia（エストニア）

あさがきた
カラフルなチョウチョ
ネコがあるきまわる

102

Bees take off
Sunny morning lures them
Each one's looking for a blossom

Čebele vzlete
Zvabi jih sončno jutro
Vsaka išče cvet

Kim Alizee Oven Lekše
age12　Female　Slovenia（スロベニア）

蜂が飛びたつ
晴れた朝に誘われて
みんな花をさがしに

Čebele vzlete.
Zvabi jih sončno jutro,
vsaka išče cvet.

Bees rise,
Lured into the sunny morning,
Every bee searches for a flower.

I went to the field
Having my hoe and digging the land
In the morning

बहिन हृलो
लएिर खेतमा गएँ
माटो खन्दै छु

くわを手に
朝の畑を
耕しに

उर्मिला थारु
Tharu Urmila
age12 Female
Nepal (ネパール)

Every morning begins with sunshine
Sunshine brings a new day
New day shows beginning of new life

・・・・・・・・・

Mansha Bhatia
age13　Female
India（インド）

朝日とともに毎日がはじまり
朝日は新しい一日を連れてきて
新しい生活をみせる

Lovely morning breeze
Such a gentle smile and kiss
We are not to miss

・・・・・・・・・

尹　烯媛
Wan Hee Wun
age10　Female
China（中国／香港）

心地よい朝の風
こんなやさしい笑顔とキス
逃しちゃいけない

Can I win?
I get up nervously
On Field Day morning

・・・・・・・・・

津田　風香
Fuka Tsuda
age 8　Female
Japan（日本）

できるかな
ドキドキおきる
うんどうかい

First rays of sun
Dew drops of pearl
Everything becomes alive

Первые луци
Капли перламутровой росы
Всё оживает

・・・・・・・・・

Valeria Kimask
age12　Female
Estonia（エストニア）

朝一番の日光
真珠のような露のしずく
すべてが生き生き

闇(やみ)が去(さ)り
月(つき)とお日(ひ)さまが挨拶(あいさつ)を交(か)わす
新(あたら)しい一日(いちにち)がはじまるとき！

Darkness has left us
Moon and Sun greet each other
Time for a new day!

Seanna Bataclan
age15　Female
USA（米国／グアム）

寝坊(ねぼう)した朝(あさ)
美(うつく)しいくちびるが
起(お)こしにくる

Waking up in the late morning
A pretty mouth comes
To wake me up

Le matin réveil tardif
Une jolie bouche vient
Me réveiller

Pariente Elias
age 9　Male
France（フランス）

目(め)ざまし鳴(な)って
きれいに身支度(みじたく)
出(で)かけるよ

My alarm is ringing
I dress myself to look pretty
And go out of the house

Mein Wecker klingelt
Ich richte mich danach schön
Ich geh` aus dem Haus

Madhu Sara Teske
age14　Female
Germany（ドイツ）

やさしいそよ風
夜明けの山を吹きぬけ
百花の香りを連れてきた

A gentle breeze
Blows over the dawn in the mountain
Bringing the aroma of flowers

微微的風兒
吹過了晨曦山頭
吹來百花香

頼 可馨
Lai Ke-Xin
age 10　Female
Taiwan（台湾／高雄）

Sunlight murmuring between the curtains
Little bird songs from the window side
From the kitchen, Mom's stew goes Bubble Bubble

커튼자락 햇빛이 소근소근
창 밖 새들이 종알종알
부엌에 엄마가 보글보글

• • • • • • • • • •

김은우
Kim Eunwoo
age 7　Female
Korea（韓国）

カーテンの間で朝日がひそひそ
窓の方では小鳥がピチクリ
台所からはママのシチューのグツグツ

The rainbow in the morning
Is so colorful
Just like a lively amusement park

ㄍㄧㄥˊㄔㄞˇ的ㄘㄞˇㄏㄨㄥˊ
ㄇㄜˋㄘㄞˇㄅㄧˇㄅㄣˋㄉㄧㄤˋㄉㄧˋ
好ㄒㄧㄤˋㄧㄡˊㄌㄜˋㄔㄤˋ

• • • • • • • • • •

盧 羿溥
Lu Yi-Pu
age 6　Male
Taiwan（台湾／高雄）

いろんないろの
あさのにじ
にぎやかなゆうえんちみたい

Birds come early morning
Pick grains and leave
Everybody likes them very much

सुबह सवेरे आती चिडिया
दाना चुगकर जाती चिडिया
सबके मन को भाती चिडिया

• • • • • • • • • •

Disha Pant
age13　Female
India（インド）

朝早く鳥はくる
穀物をついばみさっていく
みんな大好き

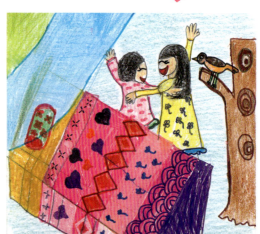

太陽はニコニコ
朝起きて運動して
すてきな一日

The sun is smiling and shining
Getting up and taking exercise in the morning
What a wonderful day

太陽嘻嘻笑
晨起運動做早操
風和日麗好

許 巧嬡
Hsu Chiao-Ai
age13　Female
Taiwan（台湾／高雄）

一日が目ざめる
暗闇を消しさって
おはようお日さま

The day awakens
Eliminating the dark,
Good morning sunshine

Julie Ann Laxamana
age12　Female
USA（米国／グアム）

びゅんびゅん走る
チーターになって
学校に遅れないように

Running like the wind
Changing into a cheetah
To get to school in time

쌩쌩 달린다
학교 지각할까 봐
치타가 된다

최 임현
Choi Imhyun
age 7　Male
Korea（韓国）

車の窓の外
谷からのぞく
まぶしい太陽

The valley couldn't hide
The dazzling sun
From piercing through the car windows

車窗外
山谷間藏不住的
耀眼太陽

朱 皓伸
Chu Hao-Shen
age 9　Male
Taiwan（台湾／台北）

A familiar smell
Is like an alarm for me
Breakfast calls my name

・・・・・・・・・

Amanda Bart
age11　Female
USA（米国／ハワイ）

いつものにおいは
目ざまし時計
朝ごはんがわたしを呼んでいる

Get up early today
The little friends are dancing
How good life is

今天起得早
小朋友们在舞蹈
生活真美好

・・・・・・・・・

韩 瑾爱
Han Jinai
age 9　Female
China（中国／北京・河北省・安徽省）

今日は早起き
子どもたちは踊っている
なんてすばらしい生活

In the morning on the couch
I read a book
Jam falls on my robe

Le matin sur le canapé
Je lis un livre
La confiture tombe sur mon peignoir

・・・・・・・・・

Le Grand Tadec
age 8　Male
France（フランス）

朝のソファで
読書するぼく
ジャムが部屋着に落ちる

太陽が私を起こし
心はあたたか
笑顔になる

The sun woke me up
My heart was filled with warmth
A smile on my face

Արևն ինձ արթնացրեց
Սիրտս լցվեց ջերմությամբ
Ժպիտը՝ դեմքիս

Դիանա Շահվերդյան
Diana Shahverdyan
age15　Female
Armenia（アルメニア）

今日はお天気
やさしいパパと遊ぶ
早起きして

Today is sunny
Play with my lovely daddy
We wake up early

蘇 喆叡
So Chit Yui
age 8　Male
China（中国／香港）

鳥たちが朝早く鳴いている
気持ちよく目がさめる
すばらしい声

Birds chirping early—
I'm awoken pleasantly
Admirable sounds

Marliani Mesa
age13　Female
USA（米国／グアム）

The bird sings
Wake up!
What a beautiful balad song

Tiếng chim hót
Thức dậy
Bản nhạc du dương

Lê Thùy Minh
Le Thuy Minh
age11　Female
Vietnam（ベトナム）

鳥が鳴く
起きて！
なんてすてきなバラードなの

I saw an octopus
Tickling my nose
Breakfast is ready

Ahtopot gördüm
Burnumu gıdıklayan
Kahvaltı hazır

Efe Aydın
Efe Aydin
age 7　Male
Turkey（トルコ）

タコをみたんだ
ボクの鼻をくすぐる
朝ごはんだよーって

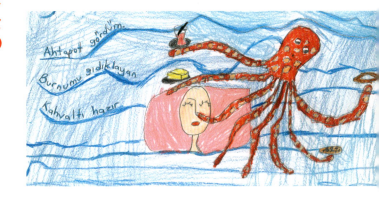

From dreams at dawn
She arrives with first chirping
In the misty field

Iz sna u zoru
Stigla prvim cvrkutom
U magleno polje

Lucija Vešligaj
age15　Female
Croatia（クロアチア）

明け方の夢から
彼女は最初のさえずりとともにやってくる
霧の草原に

Under an azure sky
Birds chirp over glad flowers
And we exercise

晴空万里蓝
鸟儿唱歌花儿笑
我们来锻炼

阎 烨辰
Yan Yechen
age 7　Female
China（中国／北京・河北省・安徽省）

晴れた日に
鳥は歌い花は笑う
さあ鍛えよう

ねぼけまなこでいると
朝(あさ)ごはんを食(た)べなさいと
おばあちゃんがどなった

My eyes half-awake
Eat your breakfast
Exclaimed grandmother

Pupungas-pungas
Kilos na't mag agahan
Sambit ni lola

● ● ● ● ● ● ● ● ●

Daniel Isaac Wong
age 11　Male
Philippines（フィリピン）

Morning on the beach
Among fallen roof tiles
The seagulls

Mañana de playa
Entre las tejas caídas
Las gaviotas

Carmen María García Moreno
age11　Female
Spain（スペイン）

海岸の朝
落ちた屋根瓦の間に
カモメ

I see many people
Working busily for the happiness of the family
During the noisy morning

ㄔㄠˇ ㄗㄚˊ 聲的ㄑㄧㄥˊ ㄔㄣˊ
看到很多人在忙ㄌㄨˋ 的工作
ㄨㄟˋ 了ㄖㄨˋ 家人ㄒㄧㄥˋ ㄈㄨˊ

劉 文惠
Liu Wen-Huei
age 7　Female
Taiwan（台湾／台北）

にぎやかな朝
家族の幸せのために
忙しく働く人たちがみえる

The dawn apperars suddenly
Playing happily in the fields
Enjoying the whole day

晨曦乍現
無限歡樂在田野
快樂一整天

張 銘禎
Chang Ming-Chen
age10　Female
Taiwan（台湾／高雄）

夜明けが突然やってきて
畑で楽しく遊ぶのよ
なんて楽しい一日

Carnival morning
A couple dancing vigorously
So much energy!

Manhã de Carnaval
Casais num só requebrado
Muita energia!

・・・・・・・

Giovana Pinheiro Valentim
age13　Female
Brazil（ブラジル）

カーニバルの朝
熱く踊る人々
エネルギー全開！

The bright sun rises
Shadows stretch across the ground
As we walk to school

・・・・・・・

Cadence Ng Chu Yi
age11　Female
Singapore（シンガポール）

明るい太陽が昇って
学校へ向かうわたしたち
地面に長くのびる影

Pancakes and sausage
Warm and steamy oh so good
Breakfast the best meal

・・・・・・・

Trevor Prause
age14　Male
USA（米国／ロサンゼルス）

パンケーキとソーセージ
湯気がたってておいしそう
朝ごはんは最高のご馳走

Daddy's face
So smooth
In the morning

・・・・・・・

持地 雪帆
Yukiho Mochiji
age 4　Female
Japan（日本）

あさだとね
パパのおひげが
つるつるよ

近年、コンピューターなどの情報・電子技術の最先端の成果として、人工知能（AI）の目覚ましい発展があり、複雑な状況認識や高度な判断を要する自動車の運転に留まらず、チェスや囲碁において世界の第一人者に勝利することや、絵画や小説といった芸術作品を生み出すことすらも可能となった旨が報じられています。このような報に接すると、科学技術への畏敬の念とともに、人間の行く末への不安も覚えずにはいられませんが、近い将来に、人工知能に代わられることのない人間としての核心部や、生きる価値や意味について考え直さなければならない時が来ることは間違いないのではと思われます。

一方、二〇一五年より世界各地において開催しました第十四回「世界こどもハイクコンテスト」。今回は、三十六の国と地域から二万六千もの作品が寄せられましたが、どの作品にも、それぞれのお国柄、文化、生活習慣などの独自性が色濃く反映されています。また、今回は、「朝」をテーマに作品を募りましたが、世界共通の事象である「朝」についても、様々な捉え方や異なる想いがあるということが個々の作品に示されています。「朝」についても、あたらしい、明るい、希望に満ちた一日の始まり、さわやかなひととき、といった捉え方が一般的ではありますが、明ける「夜」にむしろ想いを寄せる作品や、心地よい眠りから覚めて学校へ行かなければならない、家の手伝いをしなければならない「朝の疎ましさ」を詠った作品など、着眼点や発想は一様ではありません。

このようにひとつのことに様々な着眼や発想を行うこと、好き・嫌い、快・不快、苦・楽といった感情や、時と場合に左右されて異なる着眼や発想を行い、また、独自の表現を行うといったことを人工知能が行うことは、かなり難しいことのように思われます。さらに、寄せられた作品には、心惹かれたこと、感じたことを「ハイク」と絵に表現し、他の人に伝えたい、感じ取ってもらいたいという表現意欲、熱意が溢れています。人工知能が、果たしてそのような「意欲」や「熱意」を持ちうるのかもかなり難しいことのように思われます。「世界こどもハイクコンテスト」は、最先端を行く人工知能と比較すれば極めてアナログかつささやかな取り組みですが、それらに取って代わられることのない「人間の人間たる所以」を守る取り組みとして、末永く継続して参りたいと存じます。

結びに、このコンテストの開催に多大なるご支援を下さいました国際俳句交流協会　国際交流基金、日本ユニセフ協会、各国大使館、外務省・在外公館、文化庁、ブロンズ新社、日本航空などの皆様へ、心より御礼を申し上げます。ありがとうございました。

公益財団法人JAL財団
常務理事　山口　順一

＊第十五回「世界こどもハイクコンテスト」は、二〇一七年に開催します。テーマ、応募要項など詳細は、公益財団法人JAL財団のホームページ（http://www.jal-foundation.or.jp/）をご覧下さい。

おわりに

Epilogue

Advances in information and electronic technology have enabled AI (artificial intelligence) to not only drive cars requiring complicated situational awareness and high-level judgement, but also defeat world champions in chess or go games, and even produce artwork such as paintings and novels. News about the remarkable feats of AI inspires admiration for science and technology, but on the other hand causes concerns for the future. I believe that the time will come for us to rethink core values of human nature, which are irreplaceable by AI, and the meaning of living.

JAL Foundation's 14th World Children's Haiku Contest for 2015-2016 attracted 26,000 drawings and haiku from 36 countries and regions. Each work vividly reflects national traits, and unique cultures and customs. They display a variety of impressions of morning, a common theme to everyone no matter where we come from. While "morning" generally conjures up a positive image, such as the start of a bright new day filled with hope or a refreshing moment, some works depict different facets such as daybreak or busy mornings getting ready for school or helping with household chores. The children were attracted or inspired, each in a different way.

It is unknown whether AI could focus and innovate from various perspectives on a common theme, show emotions of like or dislike, pleasant or unpleasant, and joy or sorrow, think and act according to time or place, or express itself independently. The works contained here are filled with the children's desire and passion to express their feelings or fascinations, and share their feelings through haiku and drawings. Whether AI is capable of expressing desires and passion is also a question to be answered in the future.

Compared to cutting-edge AI technology, the World Children's Haiku Contest may be an old-fashioned and modest effort. But we would like to continue this project as long as possible in order to protect "what makes humans human," that is, values which are irreplaceable by AI.

In closing, I would like to express my sincere appreciation for the generous support of the International Haiku Association, The Japan Foundation, the Japan Committee for UNICEF, foreign embassies in Japan, the Ministry of Foreign Affairs, Embassies and Consulates of Japan, the Agency for Cultural Affairs, Bronze Publishing Inc., and Japan Airlines for making this contest possible.

Junichi Yamaguchi
Managing Director
JAL Foundation

The 15th "World Children's Haiku Contest" will be held in 2017. For more details, please visit the JAL Foundation website. (http://www.jal-foundation.or.jp/)

Aufa Rajihah Bt Mahadi 88
Nur Balqis Maisara Bt Arbain 117, 120

Mongol モンゴル
Uuganchimeg A 表紙 / Front Cover
Chiluugen E 7
Nomin T 15
Bilbuundalai M 16
Nandin-Erdene B 19
Sundermaa M 20
Guntumur Kh 31
Jargalmaa G 59
Unubold O 74
Javkhlant B 75

Nepal ネパール
Tharu Urmila 104

Netherlands オランダ
Nasya Weigand 37

Philippines フィリピン
Mary Jane Bayawa 11
Daniel Isaac Wong 113

Portugal ポルトガル
Fábio Miguel Brandão Lopes 80
Hugo Trindade 85
Margarida Campos 95

Romania ルーマニア
Giuglea Eliza 11
Pacea Ion 34
Grigore Daria 43
Meilă Alesia 50
Cazaciuc Fabiana 92

Russia ロシア
Anri Imnadze 20
Michael Matruk 68
Nikolai Frolov 87
Galina Tarakanova 93

Senegal セネガル
Seck Mohamed Gaye 扉 /Front Page, 120
Parrot Astrid 15
Acogny Moussa 36
Diagne Cheikh Tidiane 77
Preira Océane 80
Ley London 92

Singapore シンガポール
Shayna Neo 5
Kate Natalie Kwan Kai-en 12
Cordelia Oh 19
Violette Evangelynne Lovell Lie 68
Sarah Leaw Xuan Lin 74
Eunice Lim Yu Hann 76
Choh Shao Ken 99

Phee Hong En Chrio 101
Tan Xuan En 101
Cadence Ng Chu Yi 115

Slovenia スロベニア
Tjaša Špec 8
Klara Lužnik 32
Denis Jereb 38
Julija Vidmar 48
Eva Prevec 55
Eva Šubic 57
Maja Žunič 59
Vida Krek 60
Vid Jušič 70
Kim Alizee Oven Lekše 103

Spain スペイン
Alba Aparicio Nériz 31
Daniela Van Gestel 40
Nikoleta Stefanova Micheva 61
Paola Font Recio 89
Carmen María García Moreno 114

Taiwan 台湾（台北・高雄）
Max Lin 15
Hsiao Ling-Shan 20
Chang Yu-Hsuan 24
Mao Hsin-Hsiang 53
Tsai Yu-Shiang 56
Chiu Shao-Yu 57
Sung Yun-Shi 66
Wang Ru-Ting 67
An Sin 76
Ho Jo-Chi 76
Liu I-Pei 79
Lai Ke-Xin 107
Lu Yi-Pu 108
Chu Hao-Shen 109
Hsu Chiao-Ai 109
Chang Ming-Chen 114
Liu Wen-Huei 114

Thailand タイ
Bootsamas Nuchtaisong 14
Chayut Boonsriwong 37
Ratthaporn Ritsong 52
Sudarut Parpo 96
Thanaporn Rattanapan 102

Turkey トルコ
Guler Kaya 16
Ezgi Boz 23
Ilayda Ecelioglu 24
Ilknur Hilal Elitas 28
Nurdan Ahmetoglu 44
Duygu Gurler 81
Zeynep Nisa Turkdonmez 82
Nedimhan Ozkol 96
Maide Avcu 99
Efe Aydin 112

UK 英国
Millie-Mae Barber 16
Aditi Sing 22
Alex Kalogerakis 32
Tanya Singh 46
Francesca Wilkinson 48
Mabelle Choong 58
Eva Pellicci 67
Aahana Jagtiani Chadha 78
Reuben Flatman 84
Harry Gupta 92

USA 米国（ロサンゼルス／サンディエゴ／サンフランシスコ／シカゴ／ハワイ／グアム）
Catherine Mae B. Basto 8
Jaqueline Boyce 17
Rylan Tanaka 24
Faith Tanaka 25
Cerila Rapadas 26
Jack Lambert 27
Kaitlyn Uemoto 27
Mia Lau 28
Renee Liang 29
Daniel Bouligny 32
Audrey Leona Harjanto 38
Rocky Gao 39
Do Won Suh 40
Olivia Kim 51
Jasmine C. Pangelinan 52
Regina Gabriela Lage 53
Emily Wong 56
Joselle Garcia 57
Poem Schway 58
Naomi Shim 60
Lulu Cole 66
Ricardo Leon Guerrero II 66
Christopher Oki 69
Candice Candaso 83
Braden Nihei 88
Jessica Jin 90
Melisa Aziminashemi 91
Nazanin Rouhighodsinia 94
Seanna Bataclan 106
Julie Ann Laxamana 109
Amanda Bart 110
Marliani Mesa 111
Trevor Prause 115

Vietnam ベトナム
Vu Quy Don 2, 120
Do Ngoc Anh 13
Luu Quang Trung Hieu 23
Nguyen Ha An 30
Vu An Khanh 36
La Vu Bao Chau 38
Pham Thuc Anh 55
Le Ha Chi 58
Ninh Quynh Nhu 81
Tran Phuong Thao 88
Le Thuy Minh 112

INDEX

36 の国・地域 — 36 countries and regions

Armenia　アルメニア
Araks Varzhapetyan　9
Ella Margaryan　19
Sevan Gharibyan　48
Eva Araratyan　51
Diana Shahverdyan　111

Australia　オーストラリア
Marianne Handoko　13

Brazil　ブラジル
Milena Mayara Tyski de Oliveira　10
Adrian Gabriel Bento　48
Edenilson Daniel de Lima　56
Nauã Gabriel Wilke de Oliveira Lima　70
Carolina Correia Della Santina　83
Fernando Fernandes de Almeida　84
Wagner Henrique Correia　88
Alexsandra Nunes de Almeida　95
Daniele Pawlak　101
Giovana Pinheiro Valentim　115

Canada　カナダ
Bronwyn Chernove　53
Katherine Reilly　63
Issis Hunt　73

China　中国（北京・河北省・安徽省／大連／香港／上海）
Luo Qingqing　26
Wu Anzhuo　33
Ye Zhenyang　34
Yang Chengrui　47
Szeto Wan Hei Cato　55
Wang Ruiyuan　59
Su Yanchen　60
Gu Chenyu　62
Liu Yuhan　63
Guo Jialin　69
Liu Jiaqi　70
Ge Fangming　71
Wong Cheuk Yiu　72
Zhang Min　74
Lau Tsz Ngo　75
Tse, Brendan Hon Ting　78
Ji Zhe　83
Lu Xuanru　87
Choi Kui Wang　89
Law Chun Wing　95
Xu Hanxi　97
Siu Cheuk Hei Matt　98
Lam Wai Yiu　101
Wan Hee Wun　105
Han Jinai　110
So Chit Yui　111
Yan Yechen　112

Croatia　クロアチア
Laura Bizjak　7
Sara Podgajski　52
Petar Matausic　64
Doris Krklec　100
Lucija Vesligaj　112

Estonia　エストニア
Liiljan Veske　7
Robin Kaikyll　23
Kadriina Kruuts　39
Martti Meen　42
Rea Haljasmae　54
Andra Helena Toomet　67
Anette Leigri　69
Liisa Tooming　72
Emma Jaer　102
Valeria Kimask　105

Finland　フィンランド
Jemina Raukamo　42

France　フランス
Miclot Erwin　49
Bentata Redouane　68
Servon Raphaël　71
Pariente Elias　106
Le Grand Tadec　110

Germany　ドイツ
Lilly Dörschel　35
Arwyn Schenk　36
Madhu Sara Teske　106

India　インド
Ruhee Parelkar　21
Avni Sethi　33
Ann Joby　44
Mansha Bhatia　105
Disha Pant　108

Indonesia　インドネシア
Mareta Rani Hapsari　94

Ireland　アイルランド
Athalia Fubara　6
Chantelle Esper　37
Emma O'Mahony　43
Niamh O'Farrell-Tyler　91

Italy　イタリア
Aurora Buonaurio　11
Yuta Furukawa　12
Ludovica Moriconi　18
Elena Francescatto　33

Giulia Petruccioli　51

Japan　日本
Akari Iki　裏表紙／Back Cover
Yuka Miyoshi　39
Hiyori Tokiwa　47
Ikuto Tagashira　64
Sota Kaneko　72
Hana Kanetake　78
Sakurako Nakagawa　89
Fuka Tsuda　105
Yukiho Mochiji　115

Korea　韓国
Jeong Yedam　31
Kim Sian　40
Choi Seohee　45
Kim Yeonsu　64
Park Chaeyun　71
Lee Chaemin　87
Kim Eunwoo　108
Choi Imhyun　109

Latvia　ラトビア
Rolands Taranenko　12
Eliza Kupruka　19
Elyse Valther　44
Davis Huskadamovs　46
Dana Biktasheva　51
Amanda Ancveire　65
Vera Maria Suetkina　80
Darta Petkune　83
Elsa Ligute　91
Jasmin Saule　96

Lithuania　リトアニア
Ieva Malinauskaite　8
Ugne Legyte　23
Rimvydas Mickus　28
Simona Stombergaite　43
Ugne Bacinskaite　46
Rosita Kalendaite　76
Odeta Venslovaite　84
Emilija Dorelyte　86
Urte Strikaite　99
Eva Fiseryte　102

Malaysia　マレーシア
Maisara Bt Hashim　26
Amni Nisrina Bt Akmal　27
Nur Humaira Bt Rhyrun Anuar　34
Muhammad Muizzuddin Bin Zaini　41
Nurul Najihah Bt Mohd Fariq　44
Nur Raif Bin Huzairi　47
Nur Arini Binti Mahazir　63
Muhammad Nabil Naim Bin Miski　75
Nur Lisa Suraya Binti Mohd Padhli　87

扉／Front Page

はるかかなた	In the distance;	Au loin	Seck Mohamed Gaye
太陽姿現し	The sun appears	Apparait le soleil	age13　Male　Senegal（セネガル）
さん然と輝く	Shines with a thousand lights	Qui brille de mille feux	

まえがき／Prologue

闇が消え	The light of dawn	Ôi buổi sáng bình minh	**Vũ Quý Đôn**
まばゆい光	Shining everywhere	Ánh nắng chan hòa khắp mọi nơi	Vu Quy Don
桃の木に	And to the peach tree	Trên những cây boa đào	age13　Male　Vietnam（ベトナム）

あとがき／Epilogue

朝	In the morning	Di Waktu Pagi	Nur Balqis Maisara Bt Arbain
学校へいく	Going to school	Ku Pergi Ke Sekolah	age12　Female　Malaysia（マレーシア）
知識を求めて	To seek knowledge	Mencari Ilmu	

地球歳時記

あさのうた
Impressions of Morning

2016年11月25日　初版第1刷発行

編　者　公益財団法人JAL財団

装　丁　籾山真之(snug.)
編　集　籾山伸子(snug.)
発行者　若月眞知子
発行所　ブロンズ新社
　　　　東京都渋谷区神宮前6-31-15-3B
　　　　03-3498-3272
　　　　http://www.bronze.co.jp/

印　刷　吉原印刷
製　本　難波製本

©2016　JAL FOUNDATION
ISBN978-4-89309-624-1 C8076

本書に掲載されている、全ての文章及び画像等の無断転用を禁じます。